The British Way of Birth

D0774584

The British Way

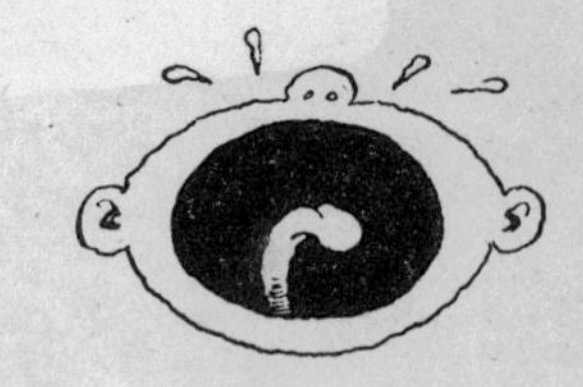

compiled by
Catherine Boyd and Lea Sellers

# of Birth

Foreword by Gordon Bourne, FRCS, FRCOG
Consultant Obstetrician at St Bartholomew's Hospital, London

Introduction by Esther Rantzen

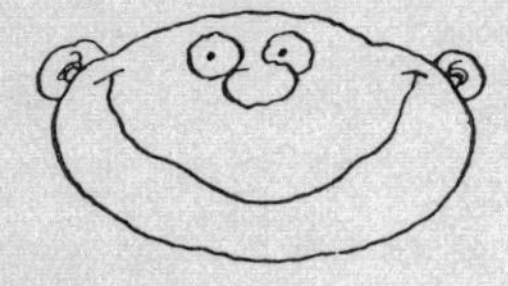

A Pan Original
Published in association with The Spastics Society's
'Save a Baby' campaign

This book is dedicated to all those mothers and babies who have contributed to *The British Way of Birth*. This is in every way their book.

First published 1982 by Pan Books Ltd.
Cavaye Place London SW10 9PG
© Catherine Boyd and Lea Sellers 1982
ISBN 0 330 26687 X
Printed and bound in Great Britain by
Collins, Glasgow

This book is sold subject to the condition that it shall not, by way of trade or otherwise, be lent, re-sold, hired out or otherwise circulated without the publisher's prior consent in any form of binding or cover other than that in which it is published and without a similar condition including this condition being imposed on the subsequent purchaser

Acknowledgements

So many people have helped in the preparation of this book that it seems invidious to select some at the expense of others. However, it is inevitable.

First and foremost we must thank the 6,000 women who have given us the raw material for the book. Without them there would have been no book.

Special thanks must go to Lloyds Bank and their computer system shop, led by Mike Weekes and assisted by Chris Craft. Lloyds Bank have donated the equivalent of thousands of pounds of computer effort to this project and Mike Weekes has acted as advisor and coordinator of the whole computer operation. The help Mike Weekes gave us in constructing the questionnaire was particularly important. Without this help much vital information would never have 'made it' on to the computer.

For the computer to collate information from 6,000 women's birth experiences it was necessary for each questionnaire to be processed or coded on to special punching sheets. This laborious but vital task was carried out by a team of dedicated volunteers who managed to fit in the task of coding with the demands of families and jobs. Each questionnaire took roughly twelve minutes.

One volunteer, May Woods, processed 500 questionnaires alone. Others who were especially hard-working included Gwynneth Robinson, Annie Bruce, Patricia Stileman, Johnnie Slattery, Mary Spraos, Cathryn Fuller and Rebecca Wood. Mary Sellers typed much of the manuscript.

We would particularly like to express our gratitude to

Kyle Cathie and Harriet Thistlethwaite of Pan Books who, from the moment we first suggested *The British Way of Birth*, have been unfailing sources of encouragement and good advice.

Finally we would like to thank our husbands (and Catherine's three children) whose patience, help and support have helped to make this project possible.

Contents

Foreword

In early 1981 Esther Rantzen decided to investigate the reaction of women to the maternity service in this country. She made her request to viewers of BBC TV's *That's Life* programme and received nearly 10,000 letters. To all of these people she sent a questionnaire to which she received a 60 per cent response. Some of the more interesting and important aspects of the response were discussed on the television programme, but obviously it took a considerable time for such a mass of material to be properly analysed and collated. The results of the survey are presented in this book which has been compiled and written by Catherine Boyd and Lea Sellers.

The authors readily admit that the survey is based on a self-selected sample. Such self-selection also tends to introduce some statistical distortions which are unavoidable when such a project is undertaken. They have, therefore, used this book mainly to reflect in both words and figures some of the experiences and predominant feelings of 6,000 women during pregnancy, childbirth and in the first four weeks after delivery.

Such a survey is, of course, a massive undertaking. The analysis of the questionnaire itself provides a great deal of useful and important information which has not been available previously, but of even greater importance is the information that can be obtained by a careful analysis of the comments that accompanied the return of the questionnaires and using these, the authors have tried to reflect the patterns, trends and opinions expressed in the responses.

It is quite remarkable that no one has hitherto attempted to assess the 'consumer response' to the maternity services throughout the country. Small surveys have been published previously, but there has never been anything approaching the size of this particular research project, nor has it previously been conducted in such a manner as to report, quite impartially, the views of the women themselves. These views contain certain patterns and themes that weave themselves together individually and collectively to produce a series of very clear and definite messages to all those who are responsible for the maternity services throughout the length and breadth of the country. The authors say, 'We hope that this book will be read and enjoyed by those interested in knowing the results of this survey, but also by those who want to know more about the way maternity services are working, so that they may be better able to make use of them.' I suggest that this book should be read by everyone who is involved in any way with the maternity services in order that they may be better able to improve the services for those who use them.

There are many interesting and important themes presented repeatedly throughout the book. Some express satisfaction with the present system, but many are critical, not only of the service itself but also of the personnel who work in it and for it. Whilst it may be easy for those who are not involved directly in the maternity service to criticize it from the outside, it is nevertheless the duty of those involved in the service to take notice of these criticisms and if possible to correct their cause. Some of the defects may be easily corrected, others are going to be more difficult to amend, whilst a few are mutually exclusive in so far as they can only be corrected to the detriment of another part of the service.

A little more sympathy, kindness, understanding and encouragement would obviously go a long way to help a lot of people, and while some readers may find this particular theme surprising, others may well have anticipated it with a degree of certainty.

Communication is a vital part of modern life and there is certainly a desperate need to increase the communication between the maternity service and those who use it. The Health Service itself tends to be somewhat inflexible and the maternity services are obviously no exception. They must learn to adjust more readily to changing demands, some of which are pointed out very clearly in this book. At the same time, society itself must adjust and alter to meet the expectations of the pregnant women today. This means not only the father and the immediate family, but also the neighbours, the community and even the State itself. The State must be continuously vigilant, for what may well have been a sufficient portion of the National Health

Service cake devoted to the maternity services in 1950 or even 1960 would appear to be inadequate in 1982.

This book also highlights the inadequate educational preparation with which most women and men face their first or even their subsequent pregnancy. Education about pregnancy should be an essential part of every school curriculum.

Esther Rantzen is to be congratulated upon the manner in which this survey was organized and Catherine Boyd and Lea Sellers upon the way in which the results have been presented.

Gordon Bourne

Introduction

It is very strange how unprepared we all are for the three most crucial events in our lives – birth, marriage, and death. Dying is still the great taboo subject, hardly ever discussed, and so all the more devastating when it shatters a family. Marriage, on the other hand, is almost too well discussed; hardly a newspaper or a magazine is printed these days without some analysis of modern marriage, or modern divorce, or modern living-together, and advice is dished out by the gallon. But it does seem very silly that when we decide to have a baby, we get so little information to prepare us for it that childbirth can be a tremendous shock, even a traumatic one.

There are books about pregnancy – Gordon Bourne himself, who contributes the preface to this book, has written a bible on pregnancy which many of us rely on, while we watch our bodies swell up like pumpkins and feel our emotions swing from contentment to panic and back again. There are even more books about child care – each one reflecting a current fashion, or the prejudices of the author. Most of us manage to find a book which chimes in with our own fashions and prejudices. But when it comes to the process of giving birth, nobody likes to talk about it in detail. So we get the vague idea that it is messy, it hurts and it is surrounded by old wives' tales. No wonder we prefer not to think about it at all.

Until, of course, it happens to us. Then we discover the truth that although it's messy nobody notices, that although it hurts the pain is bearable as long as we know exactly what is happening, that the old wives' tales which everybody advised us to ignore are usually quite true, and that everything is happening so fast that people are taking decisions we don't understand, without listening to our questions, and certainly without asking our opinion.

The people who take the decisions while you are having a baby are, of course, the professionals – the midwives and the doctors, and if you imagine yourself in their position you realize how difficult it is for them. The reason they don't listen to your questions and don't ask for your opinions is that they haven't the time – when an emergency arises they must deal with it at once, there's no time to discuss it. And anyway, the last person they would discuss it with is the patient. After all, they're working as hard as they can on her behalf, using all their skill, training and expertise. She is a completely inexperienced amateur. What does she know, anyway?

The answer is, she knows how she feels. Those feelings can be crucially important to her health and the safety of her baby. How the mother and, of course, the father feel about their antenatal care will decide whether or not she attends her clinic, takes her vitamin pills, goes to relaxation classes, whether potential problems are detected, and a baby at risk is protected. How frightened she feels may determine whether she trusts and talks to her doctors and midwives, whether she wants painkillers, whether she wants to hold her brand new baby or not, whether she wants to persevere with breastfeeding or would prefer not. The experts can give advice – but whether she can take their advice depends on how she feels.

That is the point of the survey we conducted on the BBC TV consumer programme, *That's Life* – we wanted to know what childbirth in this country feels like, to the people who experience it. It is astonishing that our survey is the first national survey of this kind. But at least now it allows the voices of the women to be heard. We hope fathers will forgive us for not giving equal rights to their voices, but, as Catherine Boyd and Lea Sellers say, it would take another survey to do them justice too.

Since the authors have been kind enough to give me credit for the idea of the *That's Life* survey, I should perhaps explain how the idea arose. I have been working as a consumer journalist on television in Britain since 1968. Over the years I have occasionally received the most heartrending letters, from parents whose babies have been stillborn or damaged at birth. When we tried to investigate the circumstances of these tragedies we inevitably ran into a wall of silence – hospitals will not supply any information or explanation to journalists about such cases, particularly when they suspect they might be accused of negligence. So there was no way we could establish whether these cases resulted from bad luck or bad management, whether they were isolated cases or symptoms of a faulty system. It occurred to me that the only way to discover the facts would be to suggest to our viewers that we might run a survey, based on their first-hand experiences. To my delight our programme editor, Ron Neil, wholeheartedly backed the idea. To my delight and astonishment, six thousand viewers enthusiastically took part and sent us completed questionnaires. Quite rightly the authors have dedicated this book to them. Without the time and trouble taken by our viewers the survey would never have been possible.

In fact, our viewers were so enthusiastic that the project nearly foundered at the start. So great was the response that it was clear that the questionnaire would have to be as complete and detailed as we could make it – but printing all the surveys and collating all the results was well beyond the resources of our production team. Perhaps God is a woman – if so, She was certainly on our side. The Spastics Society, represented by Catherine Boyd, came to our assistance – feeling that the information obtained by a survey of this kind might well be useful in research to combat perinatal mortality and avoidable handicap. They supported us with advice and practical help. Without them, the survey would never have been possible. Even then it could still have failed, if a troop of local Girl Guides hadn't come in at the last moment to put thousands of surveys into envelopes, so that they could be sent off in time.

A most important aspect of the survey is that the women who volunteered to take part did so at a very early stage in their pregnancy. We did not include women who had already had their babies, nor did we include the hundreds of letters we received from women who had had bad birth experiences, because we felt that they would tilt the balance towards those who had problems. This is not a survey based on complaints. The women who volunteered to take part did so at a time when nobody knew whether their story would end happily or not. And although, as the authors say, the survey is not a statistically measured cross-section of the population, in terms of income or geographical grouping, the extraordinary thing is that most of the results are within one per cent of the national average. So the *That's Life* survey is a very accurate picture of the British way of birth – it cannot be dismissed as an unrepresentative handful of complaints. Anyway, by far the majority of the stories end very happily indeed, with cherished, healthy babies.

But anyone who has had a baby in the last few years will recognise some of the sad experiences vividly described by the *That's Life* viewers – the 'cattle market' hospital clinics, the impossible four-hourly baby-feeding hospital routine, the midwife who refuses to believe a baby is really on the way no matter how hard a mother tries to tell her, the routine episiotomy, the routine 'flat-on-your-back' position for labour, the routine exclusion of a father as soon as forceps appear, and so on. Not that any of these are evils in themselves, just that they are now being imposed on hundreds of women who would prefer to have the choice, and to choose another way.

There are individual cases which may make the reader quite angry. Why should an army wife be deprived of her husband when their baby is born because birth, unlike death, does not qualify him for compassionate leave? Why should a wife wait hours for her husband to get home and drive her to hospital, because the ambulance refuses to cross county borders and take her there? Why should a healthy normal baby be taken away from a mother who longs for him, and kept in a nursery? Why should a pregnant woman working in a factory be made to continue lifting heavy objects until she has a threatened miscarriage? Why should a women feel her baby die in her womb, while the midwife blames a faulty foetal monitor? There must be ways of avoiding these cases happening again, if only the decision-makers will listen to the voices of the women in this book.

After all, there are many, many voices raised in praise, too. So many individual doctors and midwives combine their skills to make childbirth a joy – 'The staff were superb' – 'I felt an enormous sense of achievement' – 'It was easy . . . I was spoken to as if I really did have a say in it' – 'I was treated with sympathy and consideration' – how good it is to read comments like those. How tragic to read what childbirth can feel like when it is mishandled – 'Undignified, painful, boring, depressing . . . I hated every moment.' What a terrible way for a new life to begin.

How can this book help to eliminate the bad experiences, and promote the good ones? Catherine Boyd and Lea Sellrs make no claim to provide hard and fast answers to every question. They do not, for instance, make sweeping statements in the 'technology' versus 'natural childbirth' debate. They do, however, point out some clear indications from the survey – the danger of over-centralization in antenatal care, for instance, the lack of individual choice in labour, and the unintentional cruelty of those staff who forget the sensitivities of a new mother. For, as they point out, this survey represents a unique opportunity for the real experiences of mothers to be heard by those in charge of the maternity services in this country. Nothing but good could come of that. The only tragedy would be if their voices went unheard. And reading this book, perhaps we will all be better prepared for that most moving, dramatic, unforgettable moment in our lives, the birth of a baby.

Esther Rantzen

1 The Story of 'The Baby Survey'

The idea of doing a survey into how women feel about maternity services in this country began with Esther Rantzen. She had received many unsolicited letters from women about the care they had received during pregnancy and childbirth so one day in February 1981 she decided to ask viewers of BBC TV's *That's Life* to take part in a survey on maternity services.

Esther asked any woman who was interested in taking part and who was at least three months pregnant to write in. The response was overwhelming. Far more women wrote in than anyone anticipated. In fact nearly 10,000 letters were received in the weeks following the programme. Put another way, almost one woman in every seventy having a baby in Britain in 1981 responded to Esther's request.

In addition to the surveys sent to *That's Life* viewers, an extra 400 were sent to a London hospital, at the request of the consultant obstetrician.

Numerous organizations, professional, voluntary and consumer, and also many individuals expressed interest in this unique enterprise. Amongst these were The Spastics Society whose 'Save a Baby' campaign has been concerned for several years with improving maternity services. From the beginning the project which became known as 'The Baby Survey' was a joint BBC TV/Spastics Society venture.

The Baby Survey was designed to cover the whole gamut of maternity services experienced by women from the moment when pregnancy is confirmed, through the birth of the baby and up to four weeks after the birth. The questionnaire itself reflected these stages and was divided into three distinct sections.

The women who went to the trouble of returning the surveys – and amazingly, nearly 6,000 did – had to wade through 29 pages and 111 questions. Some questions were straightforward, such as, 'Were you visited at home by a midwife during your pregnancy?'; other questions such as 'Did you find your GP helpful and sympathetic during your pregnancy?' required more thought.

The variety and breadth of the questions reflected our concern that the survey should reveal not only the basic facts about birth in Britain today but also women's subjective reactions to the care they received. Spaces were also left for women to comment in their own words on their care and general feelings. It is these comments which form the basis of much of the book. We are truly grateful to all of the women who have gone to immense trouble to fill out the surveys. Without their efforts The Baby Survey would never have been anything more than a 'mad idea'.

The Baby Survey was designed in consultation with obstetricians and specialists in medical statistics. But any weaknesses in the survey are entirely the responsibility of the authors. And there are a few weaknesses. Some questions were wrongly phrased or lacked clarity so that we did not always get the answers we sought. For example, the list of people who might have advised women on postnatal exercises did not include mention of a physiotherapist, and the drugs and foetal monitoring questions precluded the possibility of indicating the use of more than one type of drug or monitoring method (which commonly occurs).

The Baby Survey is not a truly statistical survey. The women who wrote in to *That's Life* are a 'self-selected' group; they chose themselves. They were not selected on grounds of age, social class, religion and so on. They selected themselves because they were interested in taking part. Inevitably this means that our survey is biased towards better-educated women. An indication of this bias is that 36 per cent of those who returned surveys were from the professional and managerial or better-off groups (social class 1 and 2). According to official figures this figure should have been nearer 25 per cent. Further, only 3 per cent of mothers in the survey were under twenty, while this should have been at least 10 per cent.

Geographically, women tended to come from the southern part of the country. Women from London, Oxford, Wessex and the South West were all more likely to respond to the survey than were women from Wales, the West Midlands, and the North. Merseyside, the East Midlands and East Anglia all produced the number of surveys appropriate to the population of those regions.

No survey of this kind, asking women themselves (not doctors or health authorities) what they feel about maternity services, has ever been done before. There have been many local surveys (by community health councils, for example) and one or two national surveys but never one with such a large number taking part and also covering all the three phases of childbirth.

Although the survey may not be statistically ideal, we believe that the results make a very significant contribution to current knowledge on the subject and should be heeded by all those concerned with the health and happiness of present and future mothers, fathers and babies.

Most of the questions in the survey required simple yes/no or multiple choice answers. All these answers have been processed and put through a computer, and the results have been quantified. See Chapter 5 for full statistical results.

The additional comments from the surveys – many of which have found their way into the book – cannot be quantified in the same way as the multiple choice and yes/no answers. However, the significance of the computer results is that we were able to select quotes not on the basis of our own personal feelings or prejudices but on the basis of what we knew about the feelings of *all* the women who took part. So the comments and the statistical results should stand together, each reinforcing and clarifying the other.

The purpose of this book is to reflect as far as possible in both words and figures the facts and the feelings of 6,000 women's birth experiences. The book belongs to the women who filled in the surveys. We have had the privilege of reading and analysing these surveys and we have aimed to do only one thing, and that is to fairly reflect the patterns, trends and diversity of what we read. We hope we have at the very least been fair to those women without whose experiences and help this book could never have been written.

One of the clearest messages to come from the survey is the *variety* of the responses we recorded. No two women are the same. Every woman has her own idea of the perfect birth, the perfect antenatal clinic and perhaps even the perfect baby!

But there are certain patterns and themes which are consistent and which constantly reappear: the highly unsatisfactory state of hospital antenatal care in some areas of this country, for example, or the difficulty experienced by women who want to have more choice and control over how they give birth to their baby.

But not all the comments were negative. There was an enormous amount of praise for doctors, midwives and other medical staff who not only took care of the women's physical health but also took the time to explain what was going on and to answer queries.

But the overriding theme of the survey, and therefore of this book, must be the desire for freedom of choice. If the mother is to retain any control over the process of childbirth, choice must be offered so that every woman can feel it is her birth, her body, and most importantly her baby.

In enhancing a woman's sense of responsibility for her own baby, choice must be available – some women want to be given fewer drugs for the delivery, some want more, some women want their babies with them at night, some do not. The diversity of women's feelings is a reflection of the intensely personal nature of childbirth.

Some women want a better community midwifery service, others may prefer hospitals but want a more personal service within them. Almost all want the right to some measure of choice in how care is organized and given.

But over and over again we find that women are denied any real choice about how their antenatal care is organized, how and where they have their baby, what kind of painkillers they have or what kind of help is available after the baby is born. In most cases women must, or assume they must, accept the status quo. It is left to chance, not choice, what kind of services are available to them. The system exists and they are not expected to challenge it.

What emerges from this is that women should be listened to – that their feelings and preferences are of supreme importance and that the imposition of rules and routines can take away from a woman the feeling that it is *her* birth and *her* baby. The way a woman feels about having a baby – whether she feels secure and reassured or anxious and frightened – can make an enormous difference not only to her experience but also to her subsequent relationship with the baby.

Doctors may feel frustrated when they read some of the comments from women. They may think they are unfair as they do not allow for any consideration of the doctor's point of view; that we are more concerned with the personal than with the medical side of things. We do acknowledge that some women may have misunderstood their situations; nevertheless, the aim of this book is to reflect what women felt had happened to them. It is about *their* impressions and *their* reactions.

This survey unashamedly aimed to find out about *women's* feelings, but this in no way means that we regard men's feelings as unimportant. Pregnancy, childbirth and childcare should be a joint responsibility. However, it is women who are the main recipients of care and it is women who will undertake the main responsibility for the new baby. It was encouraging to find so many fathers playing such an active part and giving help and support to their wives. But another survey is needed if we are to find out more about men's reactions to becoming fathers.

We hope that this book will be read and enjoyed by those who are interested in knowing the results of this survey, but also by those who want to know more about the way maternity services are working so that they may be better able to make use of them.

We also hope that by spreading the word – by informing people about the variety of ways in which care is provided – medical authorities, voluntary organizations and women will be stimulated to initiate improvements in their areas and thus to widen choice.

2 Options and Objections – the Months Before Birth

For many women, becoming pregnant for the first time is the supreme achievement, the fulfilment of a long-awaited dream. For others, pregnancy happens all too easily – perhaps before it is wished for. The differing feelings women have about their newly discovered pregnancy can profoundly affect their attitude to the subsequent months of pregnancy, childbirth and motherhood.

This chapter is about the months before the birth – usually referred to bleakly as pregnancy or the antenatal period. Such clinical words are inappropriate and belie the true nature of the experience. The months before the birth of a child are unique and extraordinary, an act of creation requiring no conscious or rational effort. A woman regards her expanding tummy with a mixture of awe and amazement . . . 'Can I really have made this thing inside me?'

Being pregnant is not a thing a woman 'does', it is something that happens to her, however planned it may be. For the first time in her adult life her body rules supreme; physical processes dominate.

But pregnancy involves emotions as deeply as it does physical changes. Support and care for women in the months before birth come from many sources: husband; family; friends; clinics; doctors; midwives; health visitors; community and neighbourhood groups and self-help. But those providing this care must never forget that pregnant women are much more than just machines for making babies. This chapter is about recognizing that women having babies need to be treated as people engaged in a normal and natural process, not as ill people or 'patients' who have something wrong which needs curing.

Widespread dissatisfaction with antenatal care is, perhaps, the most important finding of the survey. The trend towards hospital-based care over the last ten years may have resulted in more healthy babies but at a heavy price, it seems, for the majority of women; where medical problems may be few but practical and social needs many.

These practical and social needs can and often are met by agencies other than medical ones. Voluntary and consumer groups such as the National Childbirth Trust and women's self-help groups increasingly offer counselling, support and advice to women during and after pregnancy – partly in response to the inability of ante- and postnatal medical services to meet wider health needs. Meanwhile antenatal care as provided by the medical authorities is the only way most pregnant women have of meeting their medical, and wider health, needs.

In 1981 antenatal care was provided in three main ways: total GP care, total hospital care and a combination of the two, usually referred to as shared care. Within this framework all kinds of variations have developed including 'domino' clinics,* midwife-run clinics within hospital and without, local authority run clinics, and home-based care. Whether or not such schemes are operating in a given area will depend on various factors, such as historical accident, and the extent to which consultants, GPs, community midwives and health visitors work as a team or separately.

Wherever and whoever provides antenatal care the likelihood is that at some stage in pregnancy women will visit a *hospital* antenatal clinic. Nearly 86 per cent of women visited a hospital clinic even if only once or twice. Ten years ago only 60 per cent visited a hospital.

The 'takeover' by the hospitals of antenatal care has been paralleled by the decreasing role of the GP – fewer women today have their antenatal care exclusively with their GP than in the past.

Has this trend towards more hospital antenatal care met with women's approval? Overwhelmingly women have told us of

* 'Domino' comes from the words 'domiciliary-in-out'. This is a scheme whereby the community midwife cares for the woman during pregnancy, delivery and in the postnatal period. When labour begins the community midwife comes to the woman's home and takes her to the consultant unit (or occasionally a GP unit attached to a consultant unit), then delivers her and returns her to her home within six hours. The community midwife then cares for the mother and new baby at home.

their dislike of hospital care and of their inability to have any real choice in how that care is arranged.

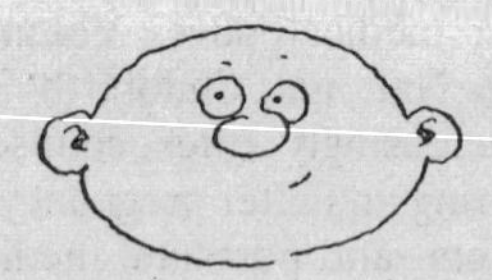

How much choice and who decides?

Pregnancy was confirmed in over 70 per cent of women by the ninth week. Only 4 per cent did not find out for sure that they were pregnant until thirteen weeks or later.

The decision as to where a woman went for her antenatal care was taken in 75 per cent of cases by the GP, with a greater or lesser degree of consultation with the woman herself. Where provision of antenatal care was limited to the local consultant unit, usually a district general or teaching hospital with no GP involvement, choice was virtually non-existent. In most cases some kind of shared care was decided on, with GP and local community midwife combining with hospital doctors and midwives. A few GPs do antenatal care without the help of a community midwife and conversely there are some community clinics run only by midwives.

One of the most striking findings of this survey is the desire for more care to be provided locally by GPs and community midwives. Women frequently did not find hospital visits worth while and questioned why it was necessary for them to go so often. The desire for more convenient antenatal care is partly explained by the increasing centralization of care into bigger and fewer places. In addition, GPs have handed over more and more obstetric care to the hospitals, and some seemingly arbitrary rules about who goes where have also reduced the options. **Gaynor**, from Surrey, said:

> *I got very tired with being made to travel right across the borough once a week to the clinic, which turned out to be totally unnecessary. Public transport is very bad and it meant leaving home at least two hours before the appointment . . . I was forced to go to this clinic as the hospital where I had my*

first baby is refusing to take antenatal cases from this area. Also my GP will not do home confinements.

We will look at the antenatal care women received in three parts – firstly the big hospital clinic (where nine out of ten women went at some stage in their pregnancy), secondly community-based antenatal care (GP and community midwife), and thirdly shared patterns of care where care was divided between hospital and community.

The cattle-market? – Your hospital clinic

Some satisfied customers?

Although most women had some criticism to make about their hospital clinic, some were very satisfied with their care. Women who found their visits to the hospital clinic rewarding tended to be those who had had previous difficulties and wanted a sense of security that everything was being done to ensure that all went well this time. Many expressed gratitude to the hospital for having enabled them to have a healthy baby. Others told of real improvements in antenatal clinics since previous pregnancies and of efforts by hospitals to introduce better clinic arrangements.

Angela, a microbiologist from Bedfordshire, expressed these feelings clearly:

I found it very reassuring that my consultant was available at hospital clinics and that he usually saw me personally. The registrars were also very concerned and I got to know the doctors who would attend my delivery. The clinic midwives were also helpful and understanding and took time to discuss any problems. Although I was excited about being a mother, I had many complications which caused me to worry, especially as I had lost my first baby and the cause of its death was unknown. High blood pressure made me tense and irritable and I felt very tired and listless.

I found that the care given me at the hospital and GP clinic was very reassuring, as I was continually tested for placental function and I had four scans to monitor growth of the baby. Discussion of my problems with my GP and my very understanding hospital consultant (who was available at clinic visits) helped alleviate these worries, but it was a great relief to have a safe delivery and a healthy baby.

Angela is a teacher from Fareham:

I suffered from high blood pressure and a need to take a thyroid drug throughout my pregnancy. The time taken by both my GP and the hospital clinic and the care given was excellent. The hospital try to make sure you see the same doctor for your last 2/3 visits in the 38th/39th week under normal circumstances.

The previous loss of a baby or physical problems which might put the baby at risk led to a much more positive response to hospital clinics. Those who could see a good reason for being at the clinic tended to tolerate its inconveniences better than those who had fewer problems and felt the local clinic could have done the same routine tests as the hospital. **Susan**, from Dulwich, is a nurse married to a hospital registrar. She felt happy about the careful check which the hospital kept on her progress:

When I visited the antenatal clinic at thirty-five weeks my baby seemed to have stopped growing so I had a CTG [a trace of the baby's heart beat], which was slightly abnormal. I was admitted to hospital for daily CTGs and rest, where I stayed for three weeks. The ultrasound scan showed the placenta to be infarcted, but as the baby was active and the CTGs satisfactory I was not induced. Everyone was very sympathetic during this very worrying period for me, and I was always kept informed of my baby's progress. I was discharged home after three weeks and asked to keep a kick count record, and, if I was at all concerned, to go back to the hospital.

Christine is unmarried and lives in Muswell Hill, London:

I found the clinic very good. The staff were all most helpful. As I had trouble with my first baby they took extra care with my second. They made me feel confident my baby would be alright and not harmed in any way as my first baby was during the birth.

Pauline, who lives in Worksop, lost her second baby from a very rare brain haemorrhage:

I would like to add that the gynaecologist is the most kind and sympathetic person I have ever met during my pregnancies.

Signs that some hospital clinics may be improving came from several reports. **Madeline**, from Walthamstow, put it this way:

My first baby was born in hospital where I was made to feel unimportant and I was never reassured. My second and third babies were delivered at home and my GPs and midwife could not have been more helpful and understanding. . .

Since writing the above statement, because my baby was breech I have had to attend the hospital, and I was really amazed at the change. I am full of praise for the staff there. I am so pleased that their attitudes seem to be changing.

Stella, from Sevenoaks, lost her baby at thirty-three weeks and expressed her gratitude to her very sympathetic consultant:

I would just like to add that all the staff I came across at Farnborough could not have been more sympathetic. I would particularly like to say that the consultant I was under was polite, friendly, helpful, spoke to me as a human being in a language I could understand and, when I knew I had lost the baby, went out of his way to come and see me (it was a Sunday) and to say how sorry he was. I cannot speak too highly of him.

Elizabeth, from Bristol, was also grateful to her hospital:

Sometimes there was a long wait but every care was taken, when you actually got to see the doctor, to explain what was happening to you and your baby. They told me to expect a Caesarean because my baby was breech up to one week before he was born and my pelvis is small. They were very fair and cheerful and tried to make you feel 'individual' even though you were one of many.

Valerie, from Chester, appreciated sympathy following a previous stillbirth:

I felt very anxious towards the end of my pregnancy as my last pregnancy ended with the baby being stillborn at thirty-nine weeks. The hospital staff and doctors were very sympathetic and reassuring. They took time to explain things properly and were very patient asking me how I felt and trying to explain why and how things happened.

So, reports of hospital clinics where the personal touch was present, and where women were treated with kindness, were forthcoming. But others simply said that they were happy to put up with inconvenience if that was what was best for the baby. **Anne** is from West Lothian:

It was very reassuring going to the hospital clinic; everyone made me feel relaxed and important. Even though there were perhaps fifteen or twenty other pregnant women in the waiting room, as soon as you went in to one of the doctors you immediately got the impression that you were the only person he was going to see that day. We were never hurried and any questions or doubts that were raised were always answered fully, and medical terms were explained.

Jean, from Ealing in London, is forty-two and a flat warden. She described her clinic as having

a very warm atmosphere. The sisters and nurses were very kind and always ready to answer questions and share their experience. The waiting was minimal and the team of doctors always very happy, cheerful and chatty. Nothing seemed too much for the staff, even tea on a tray after my session with the doctor (I had to go to the early clinic at 8.00 a.m.). My husband got a cup too! I always went home glad that I had been checked over and feeling very much in safe hands. I have assumed that all hospitals are the same and it never really occurred to me how lucky I was until I spoke recently to other women at the baby clinic. But I believe in giving praise where it is due and do hope you feel able to compliment Hammersmith on their care and concern.

Nadia was an 'older' mother, from Nottinghamshire, who particularly valued the extra concern that was shown for her at the hospital. She is forty-two:

My first baby was born whilst I was still unmarried twenty-two years ago, so I was unable to enjoy the pregnancy as such. This baby has been prayed for since we married three years ago. We were over the moon when we first had the positive result. From then on I have really enjoyed being pregnant. Unfortunately my blood pressure went up so I spent the odd week or two in hospital for total rest but never regretted it. I have been treated like a queen, as all the other patients were.

Janet, from Cheshire, seemed happy to accept the long waits:

From the beginning they made you feel important and responsible for the child you were carrying, even though the check-ups themselves usually took only a few minutes. The staff made you feel you had done the right thing for your baby and yourself by attending, and the long waiting periods were worth it. Only once did I think it was a waste of time. I had waited two hours to see an unsociable doctor who took ten seconds to give me a check-up!

Maureen, from Par in Cornwall, is a teacher. She felt that, at her hospital, attitudes improved when circumstances became difficult:

The check-ups at my doctor's clinic were always OK, with a minimum of waiting. At the hospital clinic I often felt that due to the numbers of patients the doctors were rushed and seemed to be off-hand. However, when it was thought that there might have been something wrong the attitude was completely different.

Sara is from Reading. Along with many women, she felt she owed her baby's life to hospital care. She was

admitted at thirty-two weeks after an ultrasound scan [placenta previa disgnosed] in clinic . . . for a stay until thirty-eight weeks and then delivery by Caesarean to avoid the risk of heavy bleeding.

Jacqueline, from Bilston in the West Midlands, said:

I enjoyed my pregnancy up to the seventh month. I went into premature labour ten weeks early. This, fortunately, was stopped by my hospital which quickly admitted me and added a drug to an intravenous infusion which relaxed my womb, thereby stopping the contractions. Without the efficiency of the hospital I could easily have had a baby which might not have lived. Luckily, though, I carried my pregnancy through until the thirty-eighth week. I was very proud to know that we have such a good hospital.

Kathryn, from Manchester, is a youth worker. Her story is a sad one but shows that large teaching hospitals can treat women with sensitivity. However, her story does reveal the difficulty hospitals have when carrying out tests which may reveal congenital malformations and when the woman has objections to a termination of the pregnancy:

They were fantastic. Couldn't fault them on anything. When I was twenty-four weeks pregnant I was told, as a result of a routine scan, that my baby was anencephalic i.e. that a part of the head was missing. I was offered a medical termination, but refused because I thought a child is a child from conception, not birth, and I could not kill my own child. I carried on with my pregnancy but naturally it became a traumatic experience from then on . . . I cannot praise St Mary's Hospital enough. They were really very, very good to me, explaining everything to me fully.

A few women expressed a very matter-of-fact approach to their hospital clinic – a feeling that the hospital is there to deal with physical and technical matters and that reassurance and explanation, if needed, should be sought elsewhere. **Anthea**, from Neasden, said:

I do not feel the need for reassurance and I don't suffer from anxiety. I feel that it is only common sense to attend antenatal clinics to monitor the baby's progress and to detect such illnesses as spina bifida.

But for most pregnant women, reassurance and explanation were a vital part of the clinic visit. Pregnancy involves their whole being – their mental, physical and social selves. A neglect of this by medical staff left them feeling cheated and anxious. But when the clinic was able to care for the 'whole person', gratitude was unstinting. **Barbara**, from Brentwood, had a very tragic history and a special need for support. She wrote:

My first child was born six weeks early underweight at 3lbs 3oz. The lungs collapsed and the child died four hours after birth. My second child died at twenty months as a result of an accident. In view of this being my third pregnancy and having had two daughters who did not survive, my nervous state was very up-and-down. However, the care I received was first-class and all the medical staff took time out to be very helpful and reassuring.

Susan, from Norwich, is a dental surgery assistant. She described beautifully a clinic where, with a little effort in organization and with the emphasis on the continuity of staff, even the largest teaching hospital can offer the personal touch. For Susan this was the best of both worlds:

We were all divided into smaller groups in the waiting area and I always seemed to have the same nurse in charge. Although in a vast maternity and obstetric unit and teaching hospital, I never felt just like a number on a card. Latest ideas and equipment abounded, but never to the point of loss of the human touch. I cannot really fault them and would use the same system again.

For many women living in inner cities where GPs do not always work to the highest or most up-to-date standards, hospitals may be the only provider of antenatal care, at least in the short term. Can all hospitals rise to this challenge and respond to women's broader needs?

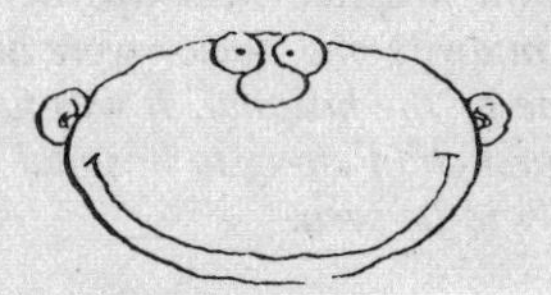

A case of antenatal overkill?

For most women the visits to the hospital antenatal clinic were far from satisfactory. There were three main reasons. Firstly they felt the visit had been a waste of time, secondly they found their visits had completely failed to help them with their 'non medical' needs, to give them reassurance or allay their anxieties, and lastly they criticized the conditions and organization of the clinics. These quotes are selected from many in which similar complaints were made.

Sandra, from Catford, told us:

I felt I was wasting everyone's time . . . theirs and mine. I was kept waiting for up to two and a half hours to have less than two minutes with a doctor who talked to me with his back to me.

Susan, from Lancashire, said:

It was a complete waste of time. I was rushed, and by rushed I mean I literally had to run down the corridor after the nurse. I was then examined in two minutes, no exaggeration, then told 'next week' and the doctor left. I was flabbergasted. It made me very upset to think how little people cared. Personally I think my antenatal care at the hospital was abysmal. They were short-staffed and each time you visited them there were more and more patients to be seen, by the same two doctors.

Karen, from Lincolnshire, had to travel fifteen miles by public transport for weekly appointments following three miscarriages:

It's time wasted in my view. I was never told anything.

And **Susan**, from Surrey, told us:

The reason for seeing the hospital doctor and my local clinic doctor was because of the problems with my first child. I, however, felt that the hospital check-ups were unnecessary because my own midwife and doctor were able to carry out all those tests done by the hospital. It was fairly difficult and tiring taking my first child along to hospital in view of the time taken actually to be seen.

Jacqueline, from Essex, spent

a very large amount of wasted time waiting to see the doctor. It also seemed very understaffed. If a crisis happened in the wards there was sometimes no doctor at all.

Jane, from Luton, complained:

It felt like being on a conveyor-belt. I saw a doctor twice and they just didn't have the time to talk. The nurses were just interested in hurrying everyone along so that they could be off duty in time. Basically the clinic was appallingly like a pregnant cattle-market . . . the only thing in my pregnancy I really disliked, and thought a complete waste of time and energy was going to the hospital clinic. I was far better cared for by my GP and his staff.

Lavinia is a teacher from Basingstoke:

Hospital examinations were sometimes so basic that they could have been done at the GP's with less all-round expense/time/bother to all parties – e.g. at thirty-eight weeks my hospital check-up was no more than my midwife would have done, but I used a gallon or so of petrol, an entire morning, hospital time and a feeling I would have been safer not actually driving that far in traffic and at that stage.

Many were concerned for the staff who worked in these clinics and wondered whether *they* felt satisfied. **Paula**, from Luton, said she felt:

like just one of too many – and the staff often seemed bored with the routine weighing and urine testing. I looked forward to going to the clinic – as another milestone in my pregnancy – and usually came away feeling an anticlimax and was it worth the trouble attending.

Madeleine, from Dorset, is an SRN. She expressed the contrast between hospital and GP like this:

As eighteen weeks had passed since my last hospital visit (I attend a GP clinic) I reported for the sake of hospital records. I had two threatened miscarriages lasting three and five days at eleven weeks and thirteen weeks of pregnancy, one following a collision with a car. The hospital doctor grinned and asked me if the bicycle had damaged the car much. He gave no reassurance as to what damage, if any, could have occurred to my foetus. He did not appear to have made any record of it in his notes. I wish I did not have to attend the clinic as I get far more genuine care and attention from the GP.

At the hospital clinic the four to five minutes actually spent not waiting was spent on BP [blood pressure], weight checks and a quick prod round the abdomen. Conversation was kept to a minimum. At the GP clinic he gave me ample time to discuss anything worrying me and answered my questions fully.

My GP gave me lots of support and comfort. I saw him on nine occasions. The five visits I had to my hospital antenatal clinic I deemed necessary evils.

Jennifer, a telephonist from West Yorkshire, described her first impression of the hospital clinic:

The first visit especially gives the impression of a cattle-market. There are times when you feel that you are unnecessary and that your baby is not yours, but theirs. You have to sit in a waiting area naked, in grotty gowns, waiting to be seen and examined. Examination cubicles are all open at the end – nurses, doctors, students, etc. – can all see in.

Asking questions, discussing problems, seeking reassurance . . . these are essential to all pregnant women, and especially those expecting their first baby. Hospital clinics too often seem unable to meet these needs. In fact, in many cases the well-intentioned efforts of hospital staff to use all modern knowledge and technology to improve the physical health of woman and baby actually result in her feeling upset and worried. Good communication between the hospital doctor and the pregnant women is the key, and too often, in the rush of the hospital clinic, this is sadly lacking.

On the whole I was made to feel very small and very stupid.

This was the way **Lorraine** felt after visiting her hospital clinic.

Brenda, aged twenty-one, from Dover, expresses this hope for her next pregnancy:

It would be lovely to think that during my next pregnancy I would be treated as a person instead of another 'case' . . . that everyone would be aware of feelings, and have the time to listen – with interest – to how one feels.

One of the most interesting and perhaps unexpected findings of the survey was the far greater degree of satisfaction felt by women about their GP consultations than those with the hospital doctor. Nearly 70 per cent found their GP helpful and sympathetic while only 40 per cent felt this way about their hospital doctor. **Alva**, from Milton Keynes:

My antenatal visits to hospital made me feel anxious but my visits to my GP clinic were always reassuring. I often went to my GP after visiting the hospital to be reassured.

Linda, from Cheshire:

I wish the consultant had explained what he wrote on my attendance card. I didn't like to ask but I did ask my own doctor to explain the symbols.

The most helpful and sympathetic professional was the community midwife (73 per cent); the hospital midwife finding slightly less approval (61 per cent). In fact all too often women were not aware of ever having met a midwife in the hospital during pregnancy. **Majella**, from Swindon, said:

Did not see her; I did not know who the hospital midwife would be.

The importance attached by women to the way they are spoken to, the little personal touches, the explained remark or test, the smiling face and, most importantly, just being listened to, is underlined by the quotes that follow. **Belinda**, from Essex, told us:

The attitude of many doctors insults the intelligence of mothers. We are entitled to know what is happening to our unborn child; tests should be explained. We should not be told that we don't need to know why they are being carried out and what they are for.

Patricia, from Manchester, agreed:

I generally enjoyed contact with clinic and doctor and sensed mostly sympathy, but felt often that the medical profession believe that nobody outside their sphere knows anything (or needs to know) about the functioning of their own body during pregnancy. Any question or comment slightly bordering on the technical was met with a look which quite clearly said, 'Oh no, not one of those women who reads books about pregnancy and childbirth,' and question or comment was then rarely answered satisfactorily.

Margaret, from Newcastle, a teacher:

The consultant assumed you were fairly ignorant, unless you showed some intelligence by asking a question which showed you had a fair knowledge of the subject. Mostly helpful, except when I asked for a scan as I felt I was rather large and wanted to know if there were two babies. He dismissed the idea, saying I was perfectly healthy and anyway if there were two I couldn't send one back.

Kirsty, from Staffordshire:

The nursing staff treated the women like children, it is very degrading. There was no literature around and no explanations given for all the various tests. Answers to questions tended to be, 'It's alright, don't worry,' but no explanations.

Lack of explanation about procedures, the position of the baby and test results was often put down to shortage of time, but many of these reports suggest an unwillingness on the part of the medical staff to regard explanation and reassurance as part of their job. Phrases like 'lump of meat on a conveyor-belt'; 'a number, not a person'; 'a number without name or face'; 'a lump to be examined'; 'no time for people'; 'very abrupt'; 'off-handed' and 'they treat us like machines' were used to describe the way hospital clinics made women feel.

Delia, from Kent, is married to an advertising executive and was having her fourth baby. She missed appointments because she 'disliked going' and felt 'too scared' to ask questions:

Because I arrived one hour early on my very first appointment due to transport problems I was told abruptly, 'You are very early, you know, the clinic does not commence for another hour.' Hardly any staff even bothered to say good morning or smile. I had felt very unwell for the first three months and the clinic was totally unwelcoming . . . The clinic is so often rushed that you feel guilty to taking extra time to ask personal questions . . . you feel too scared to ask or you forget due to haste.

And **Linda**, from Essex, said:

I think things could be a lot more enjoyable if the staff made a little more effort to put us expectant mums at ease, and talk to us and explain things and not treat us like machines.

The tendency for hospital staff to concentrate on the physical aspects of pregnancy at the expense of broader needs is demonstrated in the following remarks. **Sylvia**, from Exeter, was expecting her fifth child:

I dislike seeing different doctors at almost every visit, none of whom know any of the personal, social matters which affect me much more than the medical, i.e. I am divorced and frequently get depressed, wondering how I am going to cope with the new baby. Yet they are more concerned with how my single kidney is coping with pregnancy. When I tell them my worries they just say, 'Of course you will cope, you've had four already,' but I do not feel that confident.

Lack of time, pressure of numbers and professional attitudes mean not only that women cannot find reassurance from the clinic but also that all too often they cannot get their questions answered. **Sandra**, from Devon, told us:

The obstetrician always answered questions with grunts and groans and you end up coming out of the antenatal clinic as unwise as you went in. Of course when I paid to see him privately last year for infertility he was very polite.

Marilyn, from Norwich, said:

While I was trying to talk to the consultant the nurse was signalling behind his back for me to get dressed and off the couch. I found it very embarrassing to put on clothes while talking to the doctor. I was hardly allowed to finish dressing before I was bundled out of the room.

Julie, from Birmingham, found the presence of a student made the consultant more informative – but *not* to her:

Doctors do not explain enough to the mother. I found that if a student was with the doctor you found out a lot more because the doctor would explain to the student (not the mother) the position of the baby, etc.

Paula is a company director in London:

Some doctors seem impatient of pregnant women – they assume they are on the stupid side. I had a serious rhesus problem at twenty-eight weeks onwards – I felt that I was not taken very seriously – my questions were not answered satisfactorily. At one point I was told that I wouldn't understand if they answered my questions.

In answer to the question 'Did you feel you could ask your hospital doctor questions?' almost half of the women in the survey said 'to some extent' or 'not at all'. And 48 per cent found their questions were always answered satisfactorily. Only 40 per cent of women found their hospital visits made them feel 'important and reassured' while 22 per cent reported feeling either 'unimportant' or 'anxious' following a clinic visit. **Gillian**, from Nottinghamshire, had lost two babies – one premature, and one stillborn. She found comfort from her own doctor but not from the hospital:

The hospital staff said you could ask questions but I felt they were always too busy . . . My GP was fantastic. He talked to me at great length about any problems I had. He even used to discuss articles he had read in medical journals. I did not particularly like the conveyor-belt system of the hospital antenatal clinic or the way the staff treated the consultant as God Almighty.

Jane, from Anglesey, is unmarried:

Any question you may have wanted to ask, you either forget or feel too intimidated to ask.

Christine is a secretary from Stockport. This was her first pregnancy and she suffered from severe backache:

I felt that I was being a nuisance asking too many questions and was always being told not to worry rather than being reassured.

The effects that a previously bad experience can have on attitudes to subsequent pregnancy are well described in these remarks. **Brenda**, from Middlesex, said:

I had a feeling of background hysteria all through my

pregnancy because I dislike hospitals by previous experience, and wanted my baby born at home. I felt it my right, but had every reason and obstacle put in the way. At first asking I was told, 'No'. If I had had any trouble with pregnancy I would of course have had a hospital delivery, but all I was told was blunt 'no's. I felt upset, cheated, and even wished to lose the child. I persisted until my midwife believed she might have to deliver me at home. Near to term I relented slightly, by asking her if she would be with me and get me home in a very few hours. She said if all was OK she would comply.

Other women too found their pregnancies worrying because arrangements for the birth did not allow for personal preferences. **Jane**, from Staffordshire told us:

Regretfully came to dislike all medical encounters. I was very upset at the hospital not considering allowing my husband to be present at the birth [Caesarean]. I had an epidural anaesthetic. Some hospitals will allow a husband to be present. My consultant just said 'Next the general public will want to watch appendectomies'. This, to me, showed that I was treated as a sick patient not as a woman giving birth who deeply wanted to share the experience with her husband.

Eileen's comments sum up the feelings of many about the hospital clinic and also point to the effect this may have on their willingness to attend such clinics in later pregnancies:

Every time I came back from the antenatal clinic I was either upset or very anxious. My main complaint is lack of personal care and lack of understanding. There is no attempt to make you feel that your baby is all-important. Lack of information can cause much worry, e.g. after internal bleeding occurs. One doctor thought it funny that when he examined me my stomach was bruised. Afterwards I thought he'd damaged the baby. I was lucky to have an understanding midwife, mother-in-law and friends, but for my next baby I won't go near hospital antenatal care.

Hilary, from Cornwall, said simply:

The hospital doctor was only concerned with producing a healthy baby, and the mothers were just carriers for his healthy babies and not important in themselves. I think he would be much happier if he could grow babies in his laboratory!

Long waits in hot and stuffy rooms . . . no refreshments . . . tired and hungry toddlers . . . long and expensive journeys . . . lack of privacy . . . all these and many more complaints are made about clinic organization. Women were frequently left feeling exhausted and in some cases did not return for the next appointment as a result. We also heard of hospitals that were not like this, so perhaps with thought and imagination antenatal clinics do not have to be this way.

Travelling to the clinic involved a journey of more than five miles for nearly 40 per cent. Fourteen per cent travelled over ten miles to get to the clinic, and 16 per cent spent over £1 on their journey. Almost half had to wait an hour or more once they got there. For only 4 per cent were clinics open after 6 p.m. and in 35 per cent of cases no refreshments were available. Fifty-three per cent of clinics provided no facilities for children. Some hospitals had no appointment system while most had one which simply did not work – at least did not work well for the women. The quotes which follow graphically illustrate shortcomings in the current organization of hospital antenatal clinics. **Linda**, from Humberside, described her clinic:

I was shunted from one room to another. Nobody spoke to you except for, 'Shoes off', 'Sleeves up', 'On the scales', 'Take off your clothing below the waist and lie on the couch'. It was so hot and so crowded and there was no place to leave your shopping bags so you had to cart them around with you.

Appointments systems, or the lack of them, gave rise to much anger, irritation and even raised blood pressure. Forty-six per cent had to wait more than an hour at the clinic, 9 per cent more than two hours. **Dianne**, from Pontefract, said:

I walked two and a half miles to the bus stop. I never waited less than one and a half hours and on two occasions I left after two hours without being examined, to catch transport home. The first visit was diabolical, leaving me wishing I never had to go back there again, due to being treated like a lump of meat.

Patricia, from Manchester:

Most of the staff were genuinely sympathetic but the overall system is hopeless. When 12–20 women are all given an appointment for 9.30 a.m., it cannot possibly work.

Barbara, from Oxfordshire, already has two children:

Occasional checks at the hospital were inconveniently timed and involved lengthy waiting. For example, a 1 o'clock appointment at the hospital: who will come at 12.30 to babysit, get a child up from a midday snooze, get two children lunch and stay for perhaps four hours?

Those who already had a child, and over 60 per cent of our survey did, found hospital clinics more frustrating places than those without. There were few facilities for those children who came and waiting time gave rise to anxiety for those mothers whose children were left behind, whether at school or with a friend or minder. **Ann**, from Worcester, said:

I did by and large enjoy my pregnancy. The only time I really hated the fact that I was pregnant was during hospital visits – when I had to coordinate everything – someone to look after my son, getting myself to the hospital, then the waiting and queuing once I got there.

Brenda, from Middlesex, is a mother of three, including twins:

I was lucky I had a midwife I took to, but that was the only reason I showed myself; otherwise I probably wouldn't have gone. To have a chance of leaving in time for my school child's homecoming I'd have to get to the clinic an hour beforehand. The wait was boring, there were no amenities for accompanying children. My twins were fed up. One was not allowed to let the children wander about or make a noise; even the magazines around were for adults. I was really disgusted and felt sorry for all other mothers in my situation.

Christine, from Worthing, describes the difficulty of taking a toddler to the clinic when tests have to be carried out in other parts of the hospital:

I hated having to trek up to the Path. Lab. for a blood test (about ten minutes' walk along endless corridors and outside in the rain) because I had my two-year-old son with me, and his cars, Lassies and teddy . . . and no mention was made of anywhere to leave all my clutter, in a private room, or safer place than the waiting room. Surely all necessary tests can be done on the premises of the antenatal clinic.

Mary, from Merseyside, was expecting her fourth child:

An absolutely appalling, unreasonable waiting time for a 9.15 appointment. I left at 12.50, having had nothing to eat or drink, nothing for the kids to do, therefore had to keep one child off school to watch my two-year-old. It feels like a factory in the hospital. You actually spend a total of two minutes with the doctor so it all seems a waste of time.

Missed appointments at the antenatal clinic (hospital or GP) were reported by more than 20 per cent. Almost half of these gave illness as the reason and 15 per cent reported cost, time, dislike and a feeling that it was 'not important to go' as reasons for not attending. The rest gave various reasons but the most significant was difficulty in looking after other children. It is worth noting that the average number of visits to a clinic during pregnancy amounted to thirteen. Eighty per cent reported that they had not missed one of these appointments.

Less well-off women were more likely to miss appointments; only 14 per cent of better-off women reporting missing an appointment while 26 per cent of less well-off women did. When women's husbands were unemployed they were even more likely to miss appointments. **Pauline**, from Studley, is eighteen. She was expected to travel twenty miles to the hospital clinic at a cost of £3.36p return on public transport. No shared care was available to her so she was expected to make twelve visits to the hospital. Some of these she missed because of cost:

They don't seem to care much about you as I would have expected with the first pregnancy.

Denise, from Northampton, is twenty-two and missed some appointments:

It was too much trouble to take my 18-month-old son when heavily pregnant, and I couldn't always find a babysitter.

Elizabeth is from Bolton. She had become pregnant following a failed sterilization:

I could not afford to go to the hospital for a spina bifida test . . . I lost a good job which I needed as we could not afford any more children. I have been ill all the time through my pregnancy. I have worried a great deal about financial problems.

It seems that women who are short of money, whose pregnancies are unplanned, and who are young, find the greatest difficulty in reaching the hospital. For them shared care is essential. In some districts it may even be possible to have antenatal care at home. This brings care and health checks to the very few who can neither get to the local clinic or to the hospitals.

The survey shows that the less well off a woman is, the less likely she is to have shared care. Her care is more likely to be entirely in the hands of her local GP and midwife. Is this because she simply cannot get to the clinic at the hospital? If so should ways be found either to help her with transport and other problems, or better still have the hospital staff come out to the local clinics?

Five per cent of women in the survey had babies who weighed less than 2,500 grams (5lb 8oz). Below this weight babies are known to be at greatly increased risk of death and handicap. But which women had these small babies? Three per cent of the women in the survey were aged twenty or under. There were over twice as many babies of low weight born to this group (11 per cent) as to all mothers. Yet these women are less likely to receive hospital care during pregnancy and are more likely to miss appointments because of travel, and child care is often more difficult for them than for the better-off and older women.

Anita, from Leeds, is a twenty-year-old sales assistant:

The clinic is very overcrowded, you can be waiting for up to two and a half hours just to see the doctor for two minutes. Plus every time you go, you see a different doctor. I'd rather see the same one every time. There are always about sixty women waiting to see the doctor when I get there at 9.00 a.m. and with only one doctor on; this is why we have to wait so long. It reminds me very much of a cattle-auction, or even tin cans on a factory conveyor-belt. You're just like a number to them, they get you in and get you out again as quick as can be. You don't have a chance to ask anything even if you want to. I'd much rather just see my local midwife, at my doctor's clinic where there's no waiting around and you can get to know her and ask her things.

Jacqueline, from Coventry, summed up her feelings this way:

I never saw the same doctor twice, they were examining you as if you were a part of a car.

And a woman from West Yorkshire described the clinic as:

diabolical . . . obviously just a number on an assembly line. Appointments commenced from 1.30 p.m. but doctors did not begin until 2.00 p.m. I never ever saw the same doctor twice. On every visit the doctor had to quickly scan through my folder and get an immediate resumé of my case . . . complete lack of organization.

The need for the doctor in the clinic to cover for the labour ward was mentioned by many as a cause of delay. **Christine**, from Cheshire:

As a result of my fifth baby being stillborn I was seen by the consultant at each clinic . . . This meant waiting some time if he was needed in the delivery suite. Some mornings there were up to 140 patients to be seen in a three-hour clinic.

Jan, from Cheshire, is a secretary. She, along with many women, felt that clinic staff were doing their best in a difficult situation:

Overworked and understaffed. They try to do a good job; they are so busy it is impossible.

But the overriding message seems to be a questioning of the need to attend hospital clinics so often for tests which could be done in local GP and midwife clinics.

Small is beautiful? – Your GP or community midwife clinic

The advantages of receiving antenatal care from the GP or community midwife were emphasized over and over again. Travelling was easier, waiting times more reasonable, children were welcome – but most important was the fact that time was available to talk, to express doubts and fears, to ask advice, and to be reassured. In the local clinic, whether it was at the GP's, or in a GP unit or a midwife clinic, women felt that *they* were important, not just as carriers of babies, but as people with responsibilites beyond those purely towards their unborn children.

The visit to the local clinic was, almost without exception, described as an enjoyable and worthwhile experience. Women felt better about themselves and their pregnancy and returned home to cope confidently with their families, their jobs and themselves. They were relieved to know that all was well with their pregnancy, but also the feeling that somebody cared, that somebody would listen to them and that what went on 'above the waist' was as important as what went on 'below' was a most valued aspect of these visits.

The personal touch

In local clinics continuity of care is possible in a way which even the best organized hospital clinics are unable to achieve. This lies at the heart of the satisfaction expressed with these clinics. The doctor is almost always the same doctor and he or she cares for the woman before *and* after the pregnancy. Perhaps even more important, the midwife (usually the same one) is always there and women get to know her and come to regard her as a friend and partner, rather than a figure of authority. (A few GPs work without the help of a midwife.) Midwives in local clinics are able to offer support and friendship in a way which is more difficult to cultivate in a hospital setting. It is abundantly clear from the comments that the midwife is a much valued figure and it is in the smaller local clinics that she is able to contribute most to pregnant women. The following quotes are selected from many which expressed similar feelings. **Barbara** is from Halifax. Her second baby was stillborn, but when she was expecting her third, she told us:

> *I regularly attended the local GP clinic – seeing both midwife and GP at each visit. The same midwife took some of the relaxation classes. Both GP and midwife were helpful and would answer any questions. The GP especially always had time, I was never made to feel I was pointless or that I was wasting his time. He always stressed the wonderful experience of motherhood, how natural the whole birth would be. I always left happy as all was going well. He always explained what he wrote on my notes if I asked.*

Jill, from Halesowen, said:

> *My midwife and own doctor always had time to discuss any problem and one never felt rushed. The antenatal clinic at the maternity home was extremely pleasant. Only the expectant mothers that were due to have babies on approximately the same date attended the clinic at the same time. This made each visit more personal.*

Amanda, from Bridgwater, attended a GP clinic:

> *When I first visited the clinic I felt very nervous but as soon as I met the nurses and midwives I was reassured that I had nothing to be afraid of. They laughed and joked with me and talked very personally to me. They never let me wait for more than ten to fifteen minutes, and whilst waiting the nurses came to see that I was alright.*

Marcia, aged eighteen, is an advertising agent. She is unmarried:

> *At the hospital you felt like a number on a list but at the GP's clinic at least the midwives got more involved; they spoke about general things as well as the care of you and your baby. They made you feel you were a person.*

Community midwives are the basis of any well-run community-based antenatal service. **June**, from West Yorkshire, shows that a shortage of money can lead to a shortage of community midwives and this, in turn, can mean that some women were never visited at home by their midwife (49 per cent were not visited in this way):

In Question 7 you ask, 'Were you visited at home by a midwife during your pregnancy?' The midwife didn't come to my home because there is only one at present in this area where there ought to be three. The shortage is because there is no money for the other two. She has to sort out priorities and then decide which of these are urgent priorities. She admits herself that she cannot hope to do her job properly or as efficiently as she would like but she has no choice . . . a sorry state of affairs, but she cannot fit everyone in, with a statutory day at the hospital once every three weeks, two relaxation mothercraft classes at different clinics each week and five doctors' antenatal clinics each week . . . I understand that the post of an additional midwife has been advertised recently.

Children welcome!

Women who already had a child or children especially appreciated the welcome that was given to their children at the GP or community midwife clinic (unlike the hospital clinic). **Linda**, from Newport Pagnell told us:

The doctor and midwife were very helpful and kind. My two and a half year old daughter was just old enough to enjoy my pregnancy with me. She was made a great fuss of when I went for my antenatal check-ups, so I enjoyed my visits.

Hilary, from Henley-on-Thames, said:

The clinic was held in the GP maternity unit by my own GP and the midwives by whom I would be looked after when I had my baby. The waiting time was usually five or ten minutes and my four-year-old could play in the pleasant waiting area with his own toys. The staff were very friendly and helpful (the same staff during my three pregnancies spread over six years).

Merryl, from Sutton Coldfield, stressed the importance of the effect antenatal care can have on older children. She was booked for a domino* delivery – she would be delivered by the community midwife in the consultant unit. Some of her antenatal checks were even done in her own home:

I felt I was well cared-for by the medical services of the authority in which I live. I enjoyed the 'community midwife' system which enabled most of my antenatal visits to be carried out at home. It meant my first child was more involved.

The local clinic can be especially beneficial for younger and less well-off women who may find a visit to hospital particularly difficult. Better-off women found their hospital doctors 'helpful and understanding', whereas fewer of the less well-off did. Women of lower income are more likely to have exclusive care with their GP than those of higher incomes: 19 per cent of the former group never went to a hospital during their pregnancy compared with 13 per cent of the latter. This may be because poorer women do not want to be referred to hospitals or because their GPs are less likely to work a flexible system with the local consultant. Whatever the reason, it seems that those whose pregnancies are most likely to develop difficulties are least likely to attend a specialist hospital.

Deborah, from North London, is twenty and her comments show how sometimes the GP clinic may be the only place a woman can actually reach:

I was mainly under my GP so once when I couldn't afford to go I cancelled my hospital appointment and walked to my doctor's.

I felt they should treat you more as a person than a number on a file. I prefer the personal visit to the GP as I am talked to and always leave there satisfied that all is well.

Continuity

An advantage which many mentioned about local antenatal care is the continuity that can exist right through to delivery and beyond. The importance of getting to know the midwife or doctor who will actually deliver you was often stressed. In hospitals, with midwives working either on the antenatal clinic or

* See footnote, p. 7.

on the labour ward, but not both, this can be difficult to achieve. Seventy-three per cent of those delivered in hospital had not met the midwife who attended them before delivery. **Jean**, from Coulsdon, felt continuity was important:

It was very relaxed – no waiting. The midwife and nurse who are to attend me later were also present at clinic.

Glynis, from St Austell in Cornwall, is a mother of three young children. The home-based and personal care she received from her doctor and community midwife may well have saved her fourth baby's life:

I was so well cared-for, especially by my own doctor and midwife and if I didn't have them to turn to I'd have gone spare. At nineteen weeks I started losing – the doctor came in no time, spent a lot of time examining me and even wrote a letter and left it for me in case I had to be admitted to hospital. He called again on Monday morning to see if I was OK. At thirty weeks I called my midwife as I was having very strong contractions and I thought I might be in labour. The midwife called the hospital and the ambulance, came to my home and she rode in the ambulance with me (the hospital was eighteen miles away). She had no idea how she was going to get back home. When I came out of hospital the midwife insisted on seeing me weekly so she could check on the pregnancy more closely. On one or two other occasions I had to turn to the midwife and I think she deserves a medal for her kindness and caring. She was super and so was the doctor.

Some reservations

Some of the problems which can arise with exclusive local care were also mentioned: problems such as GPs who are not up to date with the latest developments or who are simply not interested, lack of cooperation with the hospital when a transfer is required, or lack of access to tests such as ultrasound, which require sophisticated equipment. **Vanessa**, from Shropshire, is a teacher:

I think antenatal care is more satisfactory with a GP and midwife if your GP has a genuine interest in maternity care, as the first GP I saw hadn't . . . then I think you should find another or, if this is not possible, insist that he does take an interest by being persistent in questioning him and the midwife on all visits. I can see why many of the 'high-risk mothers' give up antenatal care after one visit, as unless you have a very persistent and determined nature you do not seem to be noticed.

Mary is also from Shropshire:

Antenatal check-ups were carried out exclusively by my GP at his practice. These I felt were quick and very efficient to ensure that everything was all right, and I was completely satisfied with the treatment and attitude towards my pregnancy by my GP.

I did request a scan however at twenty-seven weeks, upon which I received a lecture on how much the equipment cost to install, and was refused.

Sheila, from Farnborough, also found exclusive GP care had its drawbacks:

I preferred attending the GP clinic as I felt more at ease to ask questions than at the hospital. He always answered queries. Every appointment always ended with me feeling a lot happier and confident that all was OK. That was until after the birth. The GP had not diagnosed twins I was carrying. I had lots of the symptoms. I feel he could have sent me for scan and I have lost a bit of faith in him since this happened.

Patricia is a chemistry teacher. She pointed to a lack of cooperation between GP and hospital:

There seems to be little contact between GP and hospital – e.g. relaxation classes and GP's antenatal class. The hospital did not tell me to go to the GP, despite not wanting to see me for twenty-one weeks. I went to the GP on my own initiative but the GP has little idea what techniques, etc., are available at the hospital.

Home delivery?

One difficulty encountered was the resistance of some GPs to the kind of delivery women wanted to have. Some even changed their GP in order to have a home delivery. Others had to battle long and hard to persuade their GP or midwife to agree. In the end only 2 per cent delivered their babies at home. **Kay** is from Lancashire:

A home confinement was requested and although my GP didn't flatly refuse to care for me under these circumstances (which probably would have been better so I could have gone to find a GP who would be more sympathetic), I felt he didn't like my asking for his reassurance and support in the matter. He never answered my questions satisfactorily – even though at times I was clearly anxious. In the end I missed visits because they made me worry so much.

There was a lot of anxiety caused through my asking for a home confinement which no one would give any encouragement for or understanding about except people concerned with NCT. * *I was in fact booked for hospital delivery but fought during the nine months up to the actual delivery for home confinement. The GP was useless and hospital staff on the whole not very understanding.*

Susan is a dancing teacher. She told us:

I saw three doctors at my GP clinic, two of whom were very reasonable. However, two weeks before my due date I met up with a doctor who was very rude and almost threatening over my choice of a home delivery. He sent me away feeling very angry and tense. Luckily, however, I only saw him once.

And **Jean**, from Croydon, said:

I wanted to have my baby at home, but my doctor doesn't do home deliveries, which is ridiculous because it's the midwife who delivers the baby, anyway. Also I'm only 5ft½in tall. I would have had more confidence in a home delivery, as the baby would have been delivered by the midwife whom I've seen at the clinic throughout both my pregnancies and with whom I have built up a relationship.

Angela was determined to have a home birth:

I had to change to a different doctor to get a home delivery. I would have liked to have one with my own doctor but she

* National Childbirth Trust.

wouldn't agree to it as she said she wasn't experienced enough. The doctor whom I changed to for maternity care was fantastic though, extremely helpful, reassuring and kind.

Erica is from Polperro in Cornwall. She was expecting her fourth baby. She wanted her antenatal care and delivery to be done locally but in her area this option was not available:

I only have to go to the hospital clinic twice or three times during the pregnancy unless the birth is overdue. The rest of the time I go to the clinic held by my doctor and the local midwife. The local clinic is good and I have a very relaxed relationship with all concerned there. I wish I could have the delivery at home because the journey by public transport from here to Plymouth involves a bus, two trains and a long walk or taxi ride the other end (it's miserable) and I know no one at Freedom Fields except the consultant (briefly), whom one rarely sees. However, home deliveries are strongly discouraged here 'especially at my age'!

Some of the happiest descriptions of antenatal care came from those who had a home delivery planned from the start and who received care from the midwife or doctor who was to attend at the delivery. **Margaret**, from Leeds, said:

As I was having a home birth I saw my own GP and midwife during each clinic visit. So different from the awful hospital clinics I experienced last time. I can honestly say I looked forward to antenatal visits; they were very relaxed, reassuring and at times humorous.

Margaret from London is a market research consultant:

Two years ago, when my first child was born, the clinic was very bad. Unfriendly and rude reception staff. Two-hour waits, scant attention, condescending attitude of doctors, insufficient information and inadequate replies to questions. This time, with my GP doing home deliveries, I was treated with courtesy and respect, understanding and sympathy. I looked forward to my visits.

The best of both worlds? – Shared antenatal care

The following thoughts come from *British Births 1970** a government supported survey, but could just as well have been written today.

> *As obstetrics has developed from an art to a more scientific speciality in the last three decades there is a suspicion that some may overlook the fact that childbirth is a normal physiological function. It is possible that improved standards of antenatal care have materially reduced mortality and morbidity for both mothers and babies; the lowest perinatal mortality rates cannot be achieved without technical efficiency but the quality of a service should be considered in humanitarian terms as well as those of efficiency. Maternal comfort and relief of anxiety are important but hard to measure. The ideal service should therefore combine these qualities.*

In their well-intentioned attempts to bring the benefits of modern knowledge and technology to all pregnant women have modern obstetricians been guilty of overkill? Being pregnant and having a baby is a normal process. By treating every woman as if pregnancy were a pathological process – something from which she must be cured – we take away her sense of responsibility both for herself and her baby. We baffle her with jargon, frighten her with machines, confuse her with tests, and make her feel that pregnancy and childbirth are far too difficult for her to be in charge of alone. And yet once the baby is born she is left to cope more or less on her own.

But for most, the problems of pregnancy are more to do with non- or only semi-medical matters. They are to do with pre-

* *British Births 1970* (William Heinemann Medical Books, 1975).

serving health, both physical and mental, and with developing the self-confidence to take on the daunting responsibilities of motherhood. If antenatal care is failing to give support in the widest sense so that women can feel good about themselves and their families, then new systems should be devised.

Can new patterns of care combine the benefits of modern know-how with the virtues of the traditional approach? So many have written wondering why more of their antenatal checks could not be carried out locally and why it was necessary to have so many checks anyway, especially during the middle months of pregnancy. A trend back towards locally-based care with coordination between consultant, GP, midwife and health visitor, and more communication between the women themselves and the professionals, would do much to meet the complaints so widely expressed. Such a trend would also widen choice. As, hopefully, more patterns of care are devised to meet presentcriticisms, so women will be able to have more choice in what kind of antenatal care best suits them, both from the medical and personal points of view.

Some of the quotes that follow show that there are places where care is arranged with flexibility and cooperation and where hospital staff even visit local clinics, thus reducing to a minimum the need for women to make frequent hospital visits. Those who described these kinds of arrangements expressed a high degree of satisfaction with their care. And yet as some of the stories reveal, the trend in many areas is towards the closing of local clinics and local maternity hospitals with more concentration of care in big hospitals. **Sarah**, from Newcastle, said:

Everyone concerned could not have been more helpful – any query or anxiety was dealt with by the midwife and/or doctor in a cheerful, reassuring manner – in fact over the duration of my pregnancy a visit to the clinic almost became a social occasion. Furthermore, the consultant from the hospital where I was to have the baby visited the clinic every month so that you were seen three or four times by him before you went to the hospital – if he considered it necessary you were asked to visit the hospital antenatal clinic for further examination. All in all excellent care and treatment . . . Everyone always had time, not only to answer queries, but also to talk about the pregnancy in general.

Reducing to a minimum the number of visits to the hospital was universally welcomed. Hospitals could then concentrate on giving a better service to women with medical problems, leaving local clinics to provide routine care for the rest. **Janice**, from Hampshire, put this point forcefully:

I do feel that although hospitals play an important part in the care of mother and baby, if your GP is willing to look after you during your pregnancy then he should. That would leave the hospitals with more time to spend with people whose GPs have especially asked for extra care because of complications. The majority of people who cope quite easily with pregnancy have their time wasted when it could be used for somebody less fortunate.

Several women wrote to us about local clinics, especially in rural areas, which consultants attended. These reduced the need for women making long, expensive journeys to hospital and also helped midwives and GPs decide who actually *needed* to attend hospital. **Laura**, from Northumberland, told us:

The consultant from Ashington came to the health centre in Cramlington where my GP is.

Valerie is a solicitor living in Oswestry, Shropshire, which is eighteen miles from the consultant unit in Shrewsbury:

The clinic is a midwife-run clinic with an occasional visit from a specialist gynaecologist when need arises. The atmosphere was friendly, the staff generally helpful. It is a small unit and the number of expectant mothers makes informality easier.

Linda, from Cheshire, described the kind of local clinic which is under threat in this and other areas:

The clinic was held in my village. The consultant came each Thursday from the West Cheshire Maternity Hospital. I only made one initial visit to the hospital, to book in prior to the birth. It was much more pleasant attending the local clinic with familiar faces rather than the hospital. I always saw the same consultant and midwife for blood pressure. I didn't find the doctor particularly easy to talk to, waiting was still quite long on occasions if they were busy, but it was by the shops and close to home so it was more relaxing.

When shared care between GP and hospital clinic works well, women express a high degree of satisfaction with their antenatal care. The convenience and support offered by the clinic round the corner, combined with the reassurance of knowing that the experts are available, give great peace of mind and produce some very satisfied customers. **Avril**, from Newcastle, said:

My antenatal care was organized mainly through my GP clinic, and I paid only three visits to my hospital clinic, to see my consultant. I cannot speak too highly of the care and treatment I received at both clinics – my doctors always working closely with my consultant. Visits to the clinics were reassuring and the staff always friendly.

Susan is a teacher from Cheltenham:

Due to three previous miscarriages I was given continuous care by a doctor and specialist. During the first eighteen weeks I was given hormone injections by my GP. All hospital staff at the antenatal clinic were extremely kind, always referring to my baby as 'precious', and gave me endless care and encouragement.

The effect that better local provision can have on reducing hospital overcrowding is brought out by **Paula** from Cumbria:

Because of the waiting time at the hospital clinic during my first pregnancy I asked if I could have 'shared care' with my GP this time. As a rule this is allowed for women having a forty-eight hour delivery in Risedale consultant unit. Both my GP and my hospital doctor agreed, and I understand that since 1 January 1981 this has become more common. I found this a lot more convenient as my GP is nearer and not as busy as the clinic. On the four occasions I have visited Risedale I found I didn't have to wait as long as during my first pregnancy.

The importance of the midwife in well-run shared care schemes was emphasized frequently. **Gillian**, from South London, describes the domino scheme. The community midwife holds her own clinic in the consultant unit where she will eventually do the delivery if no problems have arisen during pregnancy. In an urban setting this pattern seems to be very popular:

I attended the domino clinic at the hospital, where I was seen by a community midwife. The midwives worked on a rota basis but I did not find this inconvenient. I found the domino clinic a very good system, much more informal.

Caroline, from Harlow, described how shared care can work when problems in the pregnancy do arise:

I attended both hospital and my GP clinic. At both I was treated with courtesy and efficiency. I was six months when my doctor suspected twins and immediately contacted the hospital for a scan. This was arranged for three days later. I am pleased to confirm she was correct.

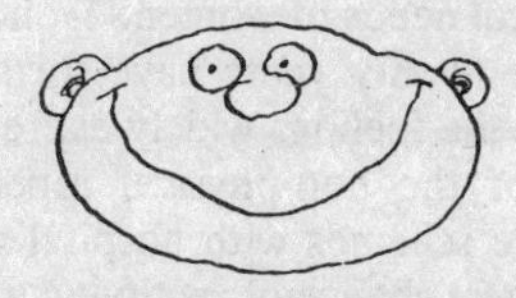

Women who had just two hospital visits, one at the booking clinic and one near to delivery, seemed well satisfied. Confidence in the care received from GP and community midwife was essential to this pattern of care. Women semed to have few doubts about the competence of their GP and community midwife. This may be because in areas where GP standards are not high or GP interest lacking, a pattern of care has developed whereby consultant units do nearly all the antenatal care. This is especially true of some inner city areas. If there is to be the option of locally-based care, GP and midwife care must be of a high standard. Where local care *is* of a high standard, operating within the framework of a team of GPs, midwives, health visitors, social workers, etc., and where contact with the hospital is direct and friendly, the pregnant woman can receive very good care. **Dorothy**, from Camberley, said:

I enjoyed going to my GP for antenatal care. The midwife was also there. She did blood pressure, urine test and weight and then I went to see the doctor. Any problems I had I talked about and he had time to listen and explain anything I wanted to know. I had two visits to the hospital, one when I was booked in and another at thirty-eight weeks.

A good shared care system allows for easy transfer of women from local to hospital care and vice versa when necessary. It is only when this can happen easily that shared care works for the maximum benefit of women and their babies. **Christine**, a secretary from Peterborough, felt that a transfer at the appropriate time may have saved her baby's life:

'Had I not visited my clinic regularly I would have been totally in the dark about what was happening to me. The care taken probably saved my baby's life due to early labour in the thirty-third week when I was transferred from my GP unit to the hospital maternity unit.

An ideal antenatal service should provide for both the humanitarian and the physical needs of women. Trends in obstetric care over the last ten or twenty years have focused effectively on physical health. But the feelings widely expressed in this survey suggest a neglect of the non-physical aspects of pregnancy. Well-run shared care schemes with hospital visits reduced to a minimum offer the best chance of rectifying many of the serious shortcomings of the present system.

How many check-ups?

How many appointments at the clinic each woman had varied widely and depended on a number of things. A very few women with threatened miscarriages, high blood pressure or diabetes visited a clinic as often as twenty-seven times, or weekly during their pregnancy. This applied to less than 5 per cent.

The most common pattern was for the first antenatal check-up, *not* the booking appointment, to occur before the twelth week (78 per cent) and for a total of thirteen visits to the clinic to occur before delivery. These appointments occurred at roughly four-weekly intervals up to twenty-eight weeks, two-weekly intervals up to thirty-six weeks, and weekly up to delivery. This pattern applied to 75 per cent.

Only 5 per cent had fewer than three apointments before the twenty-eighth week, 8 per cent had fewer than three between twenty-nine and thirty-six weeks and 11 per cent less than three between thirty-seven weeks and delivery. Some of these delivered prematurely and therefore had fewer check-ups in later pregnancy. As few as 5 per cent had their first check-up after the sixteenth week and only 2 per cent after twenty weeks. The average for the first check-up was 11 weeks.

Checks, tests and screening

At these check-ups certain examinations were almost universally given. Weight, urine test, blood pressure and abdomen examination were all done in over 95 per cent of first and subsequent clinic visits.

Examinations which were less widely done at the first check-up included height (80 per cent), legs and ankles (74 per cent), chest, with stethoscope, (61 per cent) and breast and internal examination (59 and 57 per cent respectively). At subsequent check-ups internal examinations were done on only 42 per cent of women. Ninety-nine per cent had their baby's heartbeat listened to but only half were able to listen to it themselves. A blood sample was taken in 99 per cent of cases at least once in the pregnancy, and in 47 per cent of cases blood was tested for possible signs of the presence of a neural tube defect (spina bifida). Many, however, did not know whether their blood had been tested for this or not, so it may be that 47 per cent is an underestimate of the percentage of women being screened in this way.

Ultrasound scans were done on 64 per cent of women and, depending very much on how much trouble the technician took in explaining what was happening, women found it reassuring to see that all was well and to be told for sure whether twins were expected or not. But anxiety did arise, following discussions about babies which were thought to be too small, that is, not growing properly. Only 1 per cent had an amniocentesis test.* This test could result in great peace of mind when a previous baby had been affected by spina bifida or where a possible Downs syndrome baby was suspected. However, when proper discussion and consultation were lacking, much worry

* An amniocentesis is a test in which a little of the amniotic fluid from the womb is extracted with a hypodermic needle. From this fluid it is usually possible to tell whether the foetus is suffering from congenital abnormalities such as spina bifida, anencephaly or Down's syndrome (mongolism).

followed the amniocentesis test. This was also true with ultrasound testing. Some of the benefits and drawbacks of having such tests done are expressed in the following accounts.

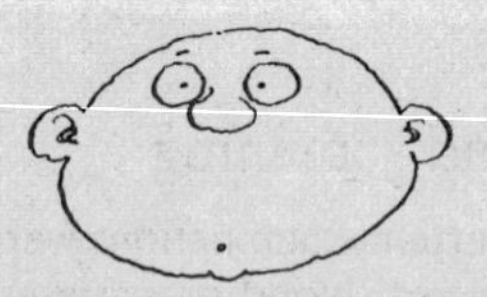

Vanessa, from Sutfolk, said this about ultrasound:

This was done by the hospital; I found it very disappointing. I was very excited about seeing my growing baby. The person who did the scan did not explain what she was doing or what she could see. She was more interested in her machine costing so much than she was in me or my baby.

Eileen is from Devon. Ultrasound was not a reassuring experience for her either:

At my last scan two people came in to discuss things over my head. I was in the scan room for half an hour and no one would tell me what was wrong. By the end of my pregnancy I was having nightmares about the birth. Staff seem to take pleasure in frightening pregnant women who are emotionally vulnerable.

Angela is a nurse in London. The doctor was concerned about the growth of her baby:

Because I had so many scans I kept thinking the baby was dead or that it would die before I gave birth. I was never really reassured by any of the doctors and I was never asked if I had any problems or worries that I wanted to discuss.

Lesley, from Sheffield, is a teacher. Her first two babies died. Amniocentesis was able to reassure her that she was very unlikely to have another tragedy:

The first baby was a girl who was anencephalic. The abnormality was such that she could not survive.

After a blood test and amniocentesis, my second baby was found to be a severe spina bifida and was terminated at twenty-one weeks.

With this pregnancy the test was done at seventeen weeks

and no abnormality was found. The sex was found to be female.

For **Margaret**, from County Tyrone, screening meant the agonizing dilemma of what to do when a serious defect was diagnosed in her first baby. In her case early screening had not revealed any problems, but at thirty-one weeks and after

countless scans and an X-ray it was confirmed that my baby was anencephalic [without a brain]. My husband and I decided to end the pregnancy early at thirty-one weeks on the advice of the doctor. My baby was only expected to live up to one week even at full term.

I was induced twice in one week . . . nothing happened the first time apart from painful contractions. On the Thursday labour was induced and my waters were broken at 2 p.m. The baby was not born until 11.50 p.m. When I was in labour the doctors and midwives could not have been more helpful and sympathetic. One of the midwives stayed with me for most of the day, refusing to leave for any breaks. I was asked if I wanted to see the baby but was advised against it. My baby (Hubert) was *anencephalic. It had been discussed with me at the antenatal clinic so I knew what to expect and the length of time my baby was expected to live, and that my husband and I would be referred for genetic counselling.*

Margaret explains her feelings in the days and weeks after the death of her baby:

Because my baby died I suffered from depression quite a lot. My doctor thought it best not to give me any type of drug because I had to face up to what had happened and I am very grateful now for that . . . a friend of mine had lost her eight-year-old girl six months beforehand and I found her a great help to talk to about how it felt, and to find out that she had felt exactly the same way even though her child had died through an asthma attack. But we both felt the same longing to touch and hold our own babies knowing that we could not. My husband was very understanding, not only by helping me about the house and having to put up with a lot from me, but because he was able to sit down and cry with *me.*

Margaret and her husband suffered terrible grief at the loss of their baby – as all parents do at the loss of any child. But perhaps the pain and anguish were slightly easier for Margaret and her husband to bear because the doctors had been able to tell her her baby would be severely deformed. To have delivered her baby at forty weeks expecting a normal healthy baby might have been even harder to take.

Women who have had, or whose close relative has had a baby with a serious defect are especially in need of sensitive and expert help before and during pregnancy. **Pauline** was expecting twins, and her experience points to the problems that insensitivity and arbitrary rules about the availability of tests can lead to:

> *When I was sixteen weeks they did a blood test and said the spina bifida level was high, but I was not to worry because it's always high in twins . . . I asked them to do an amniocentesis on me, as my sister's first baby was spina bifida but they refused to do it . . . the first twin was born a spina bifida. I blame the hospital for my daughter's handicap as I did ask for the amniocentesis . . . the hospital kept saying how sorry they were!*

Pamela, a teacher from Kent, wrote:

> *After the death of my second baby, I returned to the local hospital for my postnatal examination. I had been advised that I should ask the doctor to refer me for genetic counselling. The doctor I saw was totally unsympathetic and quite unaware that I had only recently lost my baby, and refused to refer me for counselling; he argued that spina bifida was not caused by chromosome defects and therefore genetic counselling would not be helpful in my case. I was extremely distressed and upset as a result of this encounter. In fairness to the hospital, I did receive a telephone call (some weeks later) from the same doctor, offering to refer me for genetic counselling. Obviously someone, somewhere along the line, had corrected him. However, by then I had suffered a great deal as a result of the visit which I had found so upsetting. The point I am trying to make is that even though I had a right to the kind of treatment for which I asked, it was only through persistence that I obtained it.*

The amniocentesis test was arranged as part of the genetic counselling which I received at Guy's Hospital. I was not eligible for the Down's syndrome test under the NHS on account of my age, so on the advice of a friend and a doctor I arranged through Guy's to have the Down's syndrome culture done privately, for which I had to pay.

Lyndis, from Boston in Lincolnshire, was concerned about variations in the availability of scanning facilities. She was:

worried about the disparity in care from various health authorities. My sister-in-law is expecting a baby at the same time in Dundee and has been scanned several times whereas I had to press for a single scan. Also a friend in Newcastle has not had some of the tests that I have.

The worry and anxiety these tests, or lack of them, can produce is a disappointing finding. But with sensitivity, ultrasound and amniocentesis can be a bonus both to the mother, father and doctor. It is not the technology that is wrong, but the way it is used.

Advice

The antenatal clinic can be an important source of advice and information. Many found antenatal classes helpful. However, many reported that the clinic did not give them advice in the right way or at the right time, and were often too late in claiming benefits, for example.

Some commented on the lack of advice available in clinics for second-time mothers – an assumption that they 'know it all' which was not always true. It is at the 'booking' or first appointment at the antenatal clinic that advice is particularly welcome, and those clinics with a special worker to give advice to newly pregnant women were much appreciated. Useful as the clinic is in giving information, it is interesting to note that 32 per cent found the best source of information about pregnancy to be either books, leaflets or past experience.

A cause for concern may be whether the young, less educated woman who is pregnant for the first time is receiving enough advice or information. A question which we were not able to cover in our survey is how far advice is available in non-English languages, especially for women from the Indian sub-continent.

Encouragement for breastfeeding was given to 78 per cent of women. Nearly half of these were encouraged by a midwife. Only 12 per cent were put off breastfeeding, mostly as a result of feeding difficulties with a previous baby.

Advice on rest was given to most women at the clinic (71 per cent). Many second-time mothers, however, pointed out how difficult it would be to carry out this advice. Seventy-two per cent were advised on free prescriptions, 61 per cent on free dental treatment, 57 per cent on diet, 48 per cent on exercise, 30 per cent on work and less than 15 per cent on holidays or travelling. Sixty-one per cent of women were advised about the dangers of smoking, but only 38 per cent about alcohol. Contact with rubella (German measles) was discussed or warned against in in 45 per cent of cases, drugs (pills and medicines) in 52 per cent and X-rays in only 24 per cent.

From the selected quotes that follow, an impression is given of too great a dependence by clinics on leaflets as a means of conveying information, and a need for more information especially for first pregnancies and younger women. Others had fewer complaints and seemed able to find out what they wanted to know through reading and asking questions persistently. **Carol** is nineteen, from Wadebridge in Cornwall. Her comments were typical of many younger women:

Yes, I did enjoy my pregnancy, but I would have liked more information because, with it being my first baby, I did not know what was going on.

Barbara, from Mansfield, wrote:

It was left to the doctor's receptionist to give me the forms to apply for free prescriptions. No other advice was given as my GP saw antenatal cases during surgery hours and did not have a special clinic. No advice was given at the hospital either, just a few leaflets about VD and family planning. A bit late, I thought!

Bobette, from Gloucestershire, was mystified by the questions on advice in the survey:

During my pregnancy I had no idea such issues were important, as they were never mentioned. I found out about prescriptions through the DHSS.

Carol, aged twenty-one, was having a baby for the first time:

Any advice I received from the clinic was the result of my asking questions or in the case of diet when I started to put too much weight on, it was like trying to get blood out of a stone. I was told to scrub my nipples with a nail brush to prepare them for breastfeeding. By the way, I didn't try it.

Rachael, from Northamptonshire, spoke for second-time mothers:

Not so much help and advice was given with this pregnancy, as I was expected to know it all as an 'experienced mum'.

Stephanie, from Derby, is twenty-one. She describes an arrangement which might well put right many of the complaints made about lack of advice:

At the hospital clinic there is a lady present who meets all the future mums and she advises you on diet, rest, exercises, etc., and will answer any non-medical problem for you.

Avril, from Newcastle, described a similar arrangement:

The first visit to the hospital clinic was very detailed. I saw a dietician and a nurse whose main job seemed to be to advise expectant mothers on services and benefits available from the health service.

It is worth noting that at twelve weeks pregnant it is already too late to give advice on, for example, avoiding contact with rubella (German measles). An advice service for pregnant women should follow on from a good health education programme, hopefully, carried out in schools.

For many women, information and especially advice was forthcoming from the antenatal class in a way that it was not at the clinic. It is clear that the class, with its informal atmosphere, is a particularly appropriate setting in which to provide advice on general concerns.

Sadly, 42 per cent of women did not attend classes. Some of these may not have felt any need for them, but there were reports of those who wanted classes and could not find any, or could not get to them. In almost all cases they are held during working hours for the convenience of hospital staff, but often it is difficult for a working woman to attend.

Classes were very popular and seem able to offer much more than just the relaxation and mothercraft traditionally associated with such classes. It is here that women prepare, learn and think about the birth and the care of their baby. They may also make new friends with whom they remain friends long after the birth. For those who have recently moved house this is especially important.

National Childbirth Trust classes were widely appreciated. Nearly every mother who had been to an NCT class (10 per cent of women did attend NCT classes) found them 'very helpful'. Some pointed to the emphasis in NCT classes on 'normality' and encouraging the confidence to be in control during labour and delivery. The small size of NCT classes was also frequently mentioned as an advantage. Some felt that National Health Service classes, whether in the hospital (38 per cent of women) or at the GP's (45 per cent) spent too little time on *practising* relaxation techniques and also on *in-depth* discussion. One woman said that the 'hospital organizers could take a leaf out of the NCT's book'!

In contrast to this were many who greatly appreciated visiting the labour and delivery ward as part of the *hospital* classes. Meeting the labour staff, testing the gas and air machine, looking round the postnatal ward all helped to dispel fear and to encourage a sense of being in control of oneself – not being just a cog in the hospital machine. Familiarity with hospital procedures and layout eased the transferral from antenatal clinic to labour ward and then to postnatal ward.

Sixty-two per cent of all those attending classes were pregnant for the first time, the remainder being in their second and subsequent pregnancy. It is surprising that as many as 38 per cent of those attending were not in their first pregnancy, suggesting again that women do not feel they 'know it all' after the first baby. It is also a reflection of the social value of these classes that so many second-time mothers attended.

Classes started for most (68 per cent) between the twenty-fourth and thirty-third week of pregnancy. All the classes covered relaxation and preparation for childbirth and 92 per cent covered parentcraft. Only 6 per cent found classes 'hardly helpful', while over half found them 'very helpful', the rest finding them 'quite helpful'. The importance of the partner attending antenatal classes was stressed many times. In 30 per cent of cases women reported that partners were not encouraged to take part. Women mentioned the inconvenience of daytime classes as well as babysitting problems as other reasons why partners did not attend. However other women preferred evening classes because their partners could babysit.

Some women who did not attend classes at all stressed problems of transport, cost, and child care as reasons for not attending. Several others said they had 'never heard of classes'. This particular remark came from a twenty-year-old wife of a soldier in Lincolnshire who had suffered three miscarriages and a threatened miscarriage in this pregnancy. Local classes, perhaps held at the GP's, might have provided much support and knowledge for her. NCT classes are less likely to be sought out by less well-off women.

The following quotes show the variety of comments made on classes, but overall reveal great appreciation for them and the teachers. **Ruth**, from Belfast, told us:

Childbirth was a frightening thought as I had heard so many horror stories. The classes gave me confidence to cope with the labour through relaxation and correct breathing techniques. Also we were shown all the equipment that could be used during labour and the actual delivery suite.

Susan, from Leicester, started her classes earlier than most. Only 17 per cent attended their first class before the twenty-fourth week.

Although I was only four to five months pregnant at the time I was able to remember the advice given, and the sister who delivered me asked, 'Did you go to relaxation classes? You seem in control of yourself,' which made me think the classes were worth while.

Christine, from Plymouth, attended classes at her GP clinic and said:

The relaxation enabled me to have a quick and easy labour as I felt completely in control.

Sharon, from Streatham, attended a complete course of classes for the first time in her second pregnancy:

Although I had had a baby before, I didn't attend all the classes for that one as I moved house eight weeks before she was born. So I went this time and found when the time came I knew exactly what to do to ease the pain.

The preparation for labour was the most valued aspect of the classes. Women seemed to find the lessons in caring for the baby less important. This may be because childbirth was of more immediate concern to them and a greater amount of ignorance, myth and fear surrounds the bearing of a child than the rearing of it. Nearly 40 per cent of women reported being told 'old wives' tales' about their pregnancy. **Vanessa** is a teacher from Shawbury:

Relaxation classes were helpful when in labour, although I rarely practised when at home. Talk on labour was very good – talk on breastfeeding and bottlefeeding average – bathing a baby average, but only with a doll, so not very realistic.

One advantage of the hospital class mentioned by several women was the use of 'real' babies in teaching bathing and feeding techniques. **Susan** from Port Talbot said:

I didn't attend my local clinic but went to the hospital, as it encouraged the use of a live baby. We went upstairs to bath real babies and were taken around the hospital, saw the labour room, met the nurses and tested the gas and air beforehand, which I found a great help. To see a baby made it worth while, whereas at the clinic they used a doll and the head kept falling off!

Rosemary is from Fareham. Her description of the hospital classes was typical:

It gave you opportunity to discuss any problems with other pregnant girls and ask any questions you wanted to. We visited the hospital together and were shown around delivery and labour wards, aftercare and premature units. We discussed what we would need for the baby, to take into hospital, we saw a film of the birth and discussed gas and air and use of pain killing injections. We were given information on breast feeding and bottle, and anything at all we asked about.

The contrast between NCT and NHS (hospital or GP) classes was described by several women. **Rona** is a teacher from Luton:

I found both sets of classes I attended useful. The NCT classes were very good in every way. The classes at the hospital clinic had the great advantage that all matters regarding the actual maternity unit were covered – including detailed visits round the labour ward, the postnatal ward, hearing and trying out of equipment used, advice on what to do on arrival, once in labour, etc. Both the NCT and hospital classes had two sessions for husbands too. I felt at both sets of classes I could ask and get answers to any questions I might have; I was surprised that the hospital classes even in such a busy unit were small (four of us) and very friendly. One of the sisters running the class even came along to see me as a friendly visit while I was in labour.

Christine is a teacher from Lancashire:

I found the classes organized by the NCT far more helpful and informative, particularly on labour and how to cope with it. The hospital classes spent far less time on relaxation and each topic and didn't give information in depth. The NCT class was smaller and had a more informal attitude and encouraged more discussion.

Barbara, from Hornchurch, agreed:

I had joined the NCT course of ten weeks and found them to be invaluable. I am sure this has a lot to do with the way I feel about the birth of my baby. I feel very confident and I am not frightened in any way. The subjects covered by the NCT classes helped me tremendously. There were twelve of us in one class and I felt I had the best advice and attention anyone could possibly give about childbirth and aftercare. Keep up the good work!

One of the most appreciative NCT customers was **Lesley**, from Manchester, who also reported on the value of the NCT's post-natal support service:

The NCT were invaluable in making my pregnancy and labour enjoyable. They give women information that helps them understand their own bodies and makes them feel important and relevant people, not people with no identity. Thanks to the NCT I have had three children completely naturally and managed to feed the first two until they were nine months, which I hope to do again. I'm sure this has helped me develop a really close relationship with them. The NCT doesn't abandon you once you've had your baby but continues to provide support – particularly with breastfeeding.

One reservation was expressed about NCT's approach by **Paula** from Luton:

They gave you much more confidence in your own ability and helped you realize that you must stand up for what you want for your baby – within reason. However, sadly it made me feel that the hospital could be more of an enemy than a friend and I dreaded my labour.

Too much concentration on preventing hospitals 'taking over' birth and on pushing for freedom of choice can lead to anxiety – and an expectation that the hospital will not let you do what you want, that drugs will be given to you without your agreement and natural childbirth discouraged. There are still hospitals and staff with these attitudes but the more natural approach is common in many hospitals and certainly the trend is in that direction.

Silkie, from North Shields, is a teacher. She did not appreciate too great an emphasis on the 'wondrous' experience of childbirth:

I personally would have liked to have been told more about how badly it would hurt, because I can cope better if I know the truth, even if the truth is bad. I am less frightened then, and less likely to panic. This seems to be peculiar to my character, other people seem to prefer not to know the bad bits in advance.

Wendy, from Surrey, would have preferred a different kind of teacher at her NHS class:

I felt that the classes would have been better if they had been given by women who had experienced childbirth and not by middle-aged spinsters.

The importance women attached to their husbands attending at least one class and the difficulties of achieving this were stressed in these quotes. **Christine**, from Maidstone, said:

I do feel that more classes should be available so that husbands can attend. Having a baby is a joint venture and the husband should be able to share in the experience from beginning to end. The times of the classes in this area don't make this possible.

Some women prefer evening classes both because it is easier for first-time mothers to take their partners with them and because second-time mothers can leave their children at home with their partner. Women in employment also found evening classes convenient. **Sandra** from Warrington chose NCT rather than hospital classes:

because NCT classes were held in the evening; therefore convenient for my husband to babysit with our toddler. I had to travel twelve miles to the nearest NCT class but the teacher was good.

Most employed women waited till they had stopped work to attend classes. Women have a statutory right to paid time off work for clinic appointments, but not for classes. **Susan**, a teacher from Cheltenham, was unusually lucky in having such a sympathetic employer:

My head teacher took over my class at school for doctor's and clinic appointments and my authority provided a supply teacher for ten afternoons so that I could attend relaxation and parentcraft classes.

Reasons for not attending classes, and 42 per cent did not, varied from 'inconvenient times', or 'I didn't need them', or 'I wasn't told about them', or 'they were too difficult to get to', to 'no babysitter'. **Lynda**, from Redcar, a nurse, felt no need for classes:

I have never attended any sort of relaxation because I've always been able to remain calm and relaxed, plus the fact I will most likely be having a section birth and will not need exercises until afterwards. When I had my last baby, which had died before birth, I had a very normal delivery and found the midwives were very helpful and told me what to do.

Margaret, from Leeds, who is a teacher, felt she was not encouraged to go:

I really wish I had gone but there seems to be no pressure or advice to do so in this area. People told me they were a waste of time. I know I would have found them useful if I had seen their importance at the time.

Alicia, from Enfield, had problems with caring for her first child:

I would like to have attended relaxation classes as I had when expecting my first child but could find no classes that had crèche facilities in the area.

Jean, from near Stroud, lives in the country and expresses the problems of going to classes when travel is difficult:

I decided not to attend classes due to awkwardness in travel. The classes began at 2.15 p.m., and living in a village buses were not regular. I would have left home at 12.00 noon, had to wait in Stroud until 2.15 p.m., classes ended at 3.15 p.m. – no buses to return until 4.30, arrival home 5.00 p.m. In all, for one hour's class, five hours were needed – I felt it was too inconvenient and tiring.

Linda, from Humberside, also lives in the country. She has school-age children. Like many mothers expecting babies, she felt a great need for the classes but, again, found difficulty getting there:

I did not go to antenatal classes as the nearest one was seven miles away and the bus service is infrequent. The classes were at 2.00 in the afternoon and that would have meant me leaving home at 12.30 to get to them, and I would have had to hang around for about an hour till it started and not been able to catch a bus back until 4.15, when my other two children would have been home from school for about two hours by themselves. I would have liked to have gone, as I went with my two girls and I found them helpful and reassuring.

A number of women said that the social aspect of antenatal classes was extremely important. **Susan**, from Glasgow, felt this was the only point of them!

I am convinced that the main reasons for antenatal classes are purely social.

It is clear that antenatal classes play an important role in helping parents prepare both for the birth and for the care of their baby. The popularity of NCT* classes shows how valuable voluntary organizations can be in providing alternatives to National Health Service classes.

Pregnant at work

About half the women in the survey were employed during their pregnancy. Most were in their first pregnancy but a quarter were in their second or subsequent pregnancy. This reflects the increasing tendency for women with children to be employed.

The ease with which women combined employment with pregnancy varied greatly depending on how well they felt, how sympathetic their employer was and the nature of their job. It seems that women working in factories, shops and hospitals had more difficulty than those in office-based work.

Employers and managers in factories, hospitals and shops were less flexible about giving time off for appointments, offer-

* Information on NCT classes from National Childbirth Trust, 9 Queensborough Terrace, London W2 3TB.

ing less arduous work and allowing going-home times to be altered.

Paid time off work for clinic appointments has been a statutory right for pregnant women since 1 October 1980. It was apparent that some employers and employees are not aware of this right or employers are unwilling to grant it. Eighteen per cent of employed women were not given paid time off work to attend appointments. In 12 per cent of cases where time off was given with pay it was given only 'with some reluctance' or 'unwillingly'.*

Overall, employers seemed to be reasonably helpful to their pregnant employees. Seventy-six per cent of women reported that their employer had an 'understanding' attitude to their pregnancy. However it seems that the 8 per cent of employers who were 'not very understanding' were more likely to be in the factory or shop than in the office.

Some reports did suggest a real lack of concern for the physical well-being of a pregnant employee. Several reports were made of employees being sacked when a pregnancy was announced.

Leaving work to have a baby happened for most women by the thirty-third week of pregnancy (84 per cent). Only 4 per cent worked after the thirty-sixth week, but many of these were part-time workers in home-based occupations.

Almost all employed women claimed the £25 maternity grant – 98 per cent.† Eighty-seven per cent claimed the maternity

* For further information you can get *Employment rights for the expectant mother* from any Job Centre, employment office or unemployment benefit office.

† At the time of writing 10 per cent of pregnant women (employed and unemployed) do not qualify for the £25 maternity grant because their employment record, or their husband's if they are married, is not sufficient. However, *all* women whose babies are expected on or after 4 July 1982 will automatically receive the grant. Claims have to be made between eleven and fourteen weeks before the expected date of confinement.

allowance. Forty-one per cent claimed maternity leave, but only 33 per cent said they would return to work. Perhaps some women claim leave just in case something goes wrong with the birth or to keep their options open. Most found out about benefits and rights from past experience or general knowledge (50 per cent) only 2 per cent from their union and 12 per cent from a medical source.

Of those planning to return to work, 20 per cent will go back within two months, 50 per cent within four months and 89 per cent within seven months. Financial considerations were the most common single reason for going back to work (30 per cent), but almost one-half said they were returning because of a combination of financial reasons and personal satisfaction. Only 5 per cent of workplaces had a crèche in which the baby could be cared for.

Women who managed to combine pregnancy with employment without difficulty often reported on the kindness and concern of their employer, and the support and sympathy of their colleagues and workmates. A kind word, help with moving the typewriter, being allowed home early before the rush hour, offer of a sitting-down job – all these were reported on and helped the women concerned to combine employment and pregnancy happily. **Lynda** is a civil servant from Dumbartonshire:

> *My immediate supervisor kept me on one job, i.e. at a desk assessing claims, rather than asking me to do the receptionist job which was tiring. She also never questioned my need to attend clinics, etc. The manager of the department seemed genuinely interested in my health and well-being.*

Vanda is a costing clerk from Huddersfield:

> *They were absolutely great at work. I was off work for three months at the start of my pregnancy, threatening miscarriage, but my employers were most concerned and kind throughout and showed that by buying me beautiful gifts and flowers when I left.*

Cynthia is from Runcorn. She said her boss:

> *did not mind if I was a little late in coming back from lunch, or if I was late in the morning. He was always enquiring after my health and would not let me do anything which involved*

the slightest exertion. He told me almost every day to take my time and not to rush.

It seems the more senior a woman is in her job the more likely she is to find pregnancy and employment easy to combine. She is more likely to determine her own schedule and less likely to have to ask anyone's permission for time off whether for clinic visits or for ill-health. **Jacqueline**, from Weymouth, is a manager of physiotherapists:

No problems at all with employer, as I was employed in a management position. Time off was not a problem.

Susan from Wokingham is a computer programmer. She describes a work pattern which is designed to enable women to continue working after they start to have children:

I work sixteen hours per week as a computer programmer from home. I work for ICL in a sector where most of the programmers are mothers with young children and work from home. The whole concept behind the sector is that it allows women with children to continue a rewarding career.

Less happy descriptions of being pregnant and employed came from women who worked in manual jobs (both skilled and unskilled). Complaints were also frequently made by nurses. Shortage of staff and inflexible work schedules resulted in few concessions being made to their pregnancy. It seems that pregnant nurses and midwives can be advising women to take it easy during pregnancy but can find it very difficult to do this themselves. **Hazel** is a state enrolled nurse:

In the nursing profession you are expected to work as fully at six months pregnant as when you're not.

Lynne, from South Yorkshire, is a staff nurse:

I worked as a nurse on different wards depending on demand. No consideration was given to the heaviness (mainly lifting patients) of the work when allocating wards, i.e., majority of time was spent on geriatrics.

Dawn is also a staff nurse:

I was transferred from a light duty ward to a fairly heavy one for no reason. When I asked to remain where I was I became upset at the attitude of my nursing officer. She more or less told me I was there to work, pregnancy or no pregnancy.

Rosemary, a teacher, found her head teacher less than helpful:

My head teacher refused to make any allowances. I taught all my lessons on the third floor (with the toilet on the ground floor) even though ground floor rooms were free and the school matron advised me it would be safer if I taught on the ground floor. I wanted no other concessions, as I expected to work to contract.

Patricia was a postal clerk. She found her boss was not prepared to make special concessions:

I found work very tiring and would have liked to work less hours but this was not possible. I often had to carry heavy tills with money unless a friend offered to do it. Bosses were not helpful over this.

Patricia, from Greenwich, had to 'take a day off on holiday' to attend antenatal check-ups. She says:

I seemed to be a burden and the supervisor made it quite obvious. I couldn't work under these conditions.

Sandra worked in a supermarket, and found rules were inflexibly applied despite pregnancy:

I was a checkout operator and we all had to put our names on a piece of paper if we wanted to use the toilet. Sometimes my friend and I (who was also pregnant) had to wait two to two and a half hours before we were 'allowed' to go.

Susan, a village postmistress, found her employer unsympathetic:

The Post Office sees pregnancy amongst sub-postmistresses as 'self-inflicted injury'. Holidays are used for confinement – we are still held responsible for all the post office work.

Janet worked for the Department of Health:

Shortly after I discovered I was pregnant, my GP put me on the sick. I worked at DHSS Middlesbrough, and the GP was not at all happy about the travelling involved (forty-six miles daily by bus). I was quite poorly throughout most of my pregnancy but my employers tended to keep ringing me up at home to chase me back to work while I was on the sick. I was made to feel I was 'skiving'.

Bridget, aged twenty-four, worked in a factory and felt that heavy work adversely affected her pregnancy:

My job entailed lifting and they were unwilling to give me a lighter job, resulting in me being rushed into hospital at twenty-five weeks with a threatened miscarriage.

Diane, from Sheffield, asked for redundancy because her employers could not find her a sitting-down job:

Before I put in for redundancy I asked the manager for a sitting-down job but they would not give me one, because my job was working a milling machine.

Paid time off for clinic visits was not automatically granted. Those women who knew of their statutory right to this did sometimes insist. **Anita** from Leeds is twenty. She was a sales assistant:

I'd never got on well with my manager because of my outspoken ways. He wasn't very pleased when I had to have half a day off to go to the hospital and at first said that I'd have to make the time up. If I hadn't known that I was allowed time off to go, I would have had to make the time up.

Rosemary, another millworker, from Yorkshire, did not succeed in getting paid time off:

They would have given time off to attend clinic, but being in a mill it's difficult to get someone to take over my machine.

Reporting a pregnancy to an employer can sometimes cost a woman her job, especially when she has only been there a short time. **Denise** is twenty and lives in Orpington. She is unmarried and worked as a secretary:

I was dismissed when I told my employer that I was expecting. I had only been at the job for seven weeks when I got the result.

Denise lives in Stanmore. She left her job because her employer's attitude to her pregnancy was unhelpful:

I had only been there for five months when my pregnancy was confirmed and at the beginning they were not at all helpful, making life very difficult. In the end I resigned at only twenty-three weeks on my husband's advice, as I was making myself ill with worry.

Going back to work after the baby's birth was the intention of one third of those women who had been employed during pregnancy – that is, about 15 per cent of all women. This figure is probably an underestimate, since those women returning to work who did not work while pregnant did not show up in the survey. More women would probably go back to work if better day-care facilities were available and if attitudes were more in favour of working mothers. But others reported that they were going back to work for purely financial reasons and would have preferred to stay at home with the baby. For unmarried women, going back to work was usually a financial necessity.

Amanda is an unmarried operations analyst in a petroleum plant. She lives in Withington:

This is a male dominated industry (petroleum) and not very experienced at facilitating activities for pregnant women who wish to return to work. They usually gave me the benefit of the doubt and were fairly understanding. But unofficially I met with lots of prejudice (a woman's place is in the home).

Lynda, from Dumbartonshire, was a civil servant. She wanted to return to work for both financial and personal reasons:

I would have considered returning to work had a crèche or even a nearby nursery been available, as we are not financially well-off on just my husband's salary. I also thoroughly enjoyed my work and would have liked promotion.

Vanessa, a teacher from Shropshire, would prefer to stay at home with her baby:

I would love to stay at home and look after my baby but my husband cannot support us on his very low income.

Those who can combine motherhood with a continuation of their employment – who do not have to choose between being a mother and being employed – were particularly positive about their future plans. **Jean**, from Ealing, is forty-two and is a warden of an elderly people's sheltered housing scheme:

As a warden of sixty-nine elderly persons occupying the whole of Bowmans Close it is felt that our new baby can only bring more joy and comfort into the lives of the old folk. They are all delighted at the prospect. My baby will return to work with me, in a sense.

Your health and habits

Smoking is known to be damaging to the unborn baby. It is disappointing that, despite much publicity and health education campaigns about the dangers of smoking in pregnancy, 10 per cent of women smoked more than ten a day. However 73 per cent did not smoke at all during their pregnancy.

One reason why the babies of less well-off women are more likely to be unhealthy at birth is that heavy smoking is more common with these women. Our survey gave ample support to this smoking pattern. Eighty per cent of the better-off never smoked, while only 55 per cent of the less well-off never smoked. Better-off women smoked ten or more cigarettes in only 5 per cent of cases, while more than 22 per cent of the less well-off smoked more than ten.

Practically every woman (97 per cent) reported that during her pregnancy she had symptoms which made her feel unwell. The most frequently mentioned symptom was tiredness (87 per cent) followed by nausea (70 per cent), heartburn (67 per cent) and backache (66 per cent). Less frequent was sickness (52 per cent), insomnia (43 per cent), constipation (42 per cent) and fainting (17 per cent). Given the frequency of nausea and heartburn, it was not surprising that so many reported taking prescribed drugs for these conditions. Seventy-one per cent of women took pills or medicine during their pregnancy, 80 per cent of them on their doctor's advice. Fourteen per cent of women who took pills took them on their own initiative.

Food 'fads' were reported by almost half the of women in the survey. Highly-spiced foods were commonly mentioned. **Hilary**, from Kent, gave a fairly typical list:

> *Sharp and acid tarts, vinegar, lemon, grapefruit, red pickled cabbage, Branston pickle, Lucozade and fish.*

Roma, an appeals organizer from London, mentioned simply 'marmite and ice', while **Alison**, from Bristol, preferred 'chips dipped in coleslaw'. **Jacqueline** from Milton Keynes also had a passion for coleslaw and Lucozade:

> *Pork pie, saveloys dipped in coleslaw, scampi, Lucozade, noodles, Chinese food, bacon and onion sandwiches.*

A lot of women simply went for what was good for them, such as orange juice, and avoided what might be bad, such as alcohol, coffee and tea.

Pregnancy – enjoyable or not?

Seventy per cent of women reported enjoying their pregnancy. Seventy-two per cent said their husbands or partners were 'helpful and sympathetic' and only 3 per cent 'not very helpful and sympathetic'. There is a suspicion that some husbands changed their wives' entries, so perhaps this 3 per cent is an underestimate. Various entries were crossed out and rewritten by husbands!

A planned pregnancy and a supportive husband stood out clearly as leading to enjoyable pregnancies. Women alone or in unstable relationships suffered from more anxiety and stress than others. Financial worry was an element in many women's anxiety, as was tiredness due to caring for other children. Many women worried about how the new baby would fit into the family and others about whether the baby could be afforded.

Instability and ups and downs of mood during pregnancy were common – one day cheerful and optimistic, the next day down and depressed. An active, kicking baby was a great source of reassurance, particularly to those who had experienced the loss of a previous baby.

Some felt ugly, while others said they looked and felt radiant. Some resented the restrictions imposed by being pregnant, others loved feeling 'special' and being cosseted by their husbands, friends and families.

Some women said they felt their pregnancy had been less than happy because of worry about the birth – hoping that the particular kind of birth they planned would actually take place – or whether, for medical or non-medical reasons, the birth would not be up to their ideal. **Alison** is a painter from Dudley. The difference a sympathetic partner can make to a woman in pregnancy is well expressed. She also brings out the mixtures of emotion women can feel during pregnancy:

I enjoyed being fitter and generally healthier than I've ever been before as the result of more careful eating and more sleep. My husband and I grew closer as we prepared for the baby. I enjoyed the extra fuss people made of me – it was lovely to be offered seats instead of doing the offering myself. One aspect I didn't particularly enjoy was the emotional upsets I had during the last 3–4 months. I would shock very easily and stupid little things reduced me to floods of tears. The first time I 'got into one of my states' we were both very frightened as I'd never experienced anything like it before. Of course the fear only made it worse! My husband was marvellous at 'picking me up' on subsequent occasions.

Ronita, from Bexleyheath, found that pregnancy brought her and her husband into a particularly close relationship. For such couples the growing baby was a wonder to be constantly marvelled at – a miracle to be shared:

My husband and I have got on so well I don't want it to end.

Carol, a farmer's wife from Dyfed, was more down to earth:

He has two children and 100 pregnant cows so he should be understanding!

Elizabeth lives in Hampshire. For her, pregnancy was a lonely time because her husband is a sergeant in the Royal Engineers, and was away:

I enjoyed being pregnant and the thought of the new baby. As with 99 per cent of army wives, much of the time is spent alone. Coping with a two-year-old, feeling tired and sick at times without a husband's support, can take the edge off the joy. Although many wives know their husbands might be away at time of delivery, mine was away till 5 March and baby was due on 4 March. It is sad that for close bereavement they are allowed home, when they can do little, but birth, which occurs perhaps two or three times in a lifetime and is a very special time, is not considered as important.

Janet, from Worthing, lost her first baby. She described the effect this had on her next pregnancy:

Everybody said I bloomed. I felt important, although there were sad memories and towards the end I felt weepy and pessimistic. I needed things to do. If I didn't feel the baby move I was concerned, but on days when the baby was active I felt very good. I needed this baby so badly and I couldn't really explain this to the hospital staff, so I felt one of a number.

Jacqueline, from Bristol, did not enjoy her pregnancy:

No, I didn't enjoy being pregnant. I felt uncomfortable, big and awkward. I had throbbing varicose veins protruding in one leg. I wanted the best for the baby, so what I ate was good and not what I enjoyed. I felt like some kind of production line at the visits to the clinic, not to mention nights of heartburn and mornings of sickness. No, all in all I didn't enjoy this particular experience in life. But the thing that made the whole thing worth while was hearing, 'Mrs C— you have a son!'

Jacqueline, from Milton Keynes, like many mothers, reported feeling depressed and ugly:

I felt very uncomfortable. Doctors wouldn't give me anything for cramp or sickness, neighbours kept making rude remarks like 'Haven't you dropped it yet?' When you were shopping people never considered you were pregnant and would bump into you. I couldn't get enough sleep or rest, therefore always felt tired and depressed because no one seemed to understand.

For some women, pregnancy can lead to serious mental stress – made more likely by an upheaval such as moving house. **Diane**, from Keighley, said:

The first few months were OK but then I moved house when five months and from then on I was very tired, irritable, bad-tempered and generally felt everything got on top of me. The last month my nerves were so bad I was given sleeping tablets and Valium by hospital doctors. Things didn't improve, so I was taken in for rest until birth. I honestly thought I was going round the bend; had they not admitted me I think I would have had a nervous breakdown. No, I did not enjoy my pregnancy.

Joan, from Bristol, felt very lonely. She had moved house:

I had no one to talk to in general – my mother is dead and my father is seventy – my husband does not seem to take any interest in my condition. We had only just moved to a new district, so I had no friend.

Susan, from Lewes, did not plan her pregnancy. Her husband is also out of work:

It was very unplanned so husband, family, etc., were very upset. After having one abortion already, I had definitely decided not to have another whatever the circumstances. Therefore I did not really enjoy pregnancy as I had with the other children, because of the general feeling of the family, mother, husband, etc., and towards the end when blood pressure kept rising, probably through worry, I had to go into hospital to rest, which only made me more anxious.

The unplanned pregnancy often became a stressful pregnancy – although women frequently described great delight when the baby arrived. **Fiona**, from Preston, wrote:

The pregnancy was unplanned – the result of taking the minipill. So apart from feeling very sick for the first three months, I bitterly resented being pregnant with two other small children to look after. It took me about seven months to really accept the fact I was pregnant, then I tried to think more positively about it.

Sian is aged twenty and lives with her boyfriend in Bayswater. She found it hard to tell anyone about her pregnancy:

I did not tell anyone I was pregnant until I was three and a half months gone. Because my pregnancy was not planned, I found it hard to disclose the fact. When I had and everyone had got used to the idea, I quite enjoyed it. There were times when I did feel upset and depressed, but it never lasted long.

Janice, from Gravesend, is a secretary. Her pregnancy was unplanned and she describes the feelings of resentment such a situation can lead to:

Unwanted first pregnancy and a motorbike trip abroad and a skiing holiday were cancelled. We found it fairly important to move to a larger house. I resented my body changing and being restricted and not having the same freedom of relationship with my husband. I resented the hospital treatment and was extremely depressed for the first five to six months. I was afraid everything we'd planned would come to an end. I felt trapped, and scared my feelings wouldn't change with birth, as I found babies unpleasant.

Perhaps the best description of being pregnant and how it feels came in verse form from **Odette**, in Hereford:

I'd like to thank you, Esther,
From mums and mums to be,
For your interest in our care
Post and antenatally.

It certainly isn't an easy task
To carry a child and give birth,
With morning sickness and blood pressure
And an ever increasing girth.

Your funny little fancies
(Sherbert fountains and cola were mine),
And swollen ankles and anaemia,
While everyone says, 'You were fine!'

You think the months will never end,
You forget when you last saw your feet,
And now, in the days of women's lib.,
On full buses you don't get a seat!

Then one day the long wait is over,
Your baby's about to arrive,
And when you're holding it, warm, in your arms.
You know it's great to be alive.

Now you find you've been promoted;
You're a mother as well as a wife,
There are two people there who love you,
That's what it's all for – THAT'S LIFE!

This chapter has shown that much is wrong with the way antenatal services are organized. A woman cares deeply about the health of her unborn baby, but clinics which exist to help her to have a healthy baby often leave her feeling exhausted and worried. Antenatal care *can* be organized so that it can meet both the physical needs of pregnant women and also their wider needs for reassurance, advice and support. At present too many women are finding their visits to antenatal clinics are making them feel worse than if they had stayed at home.

Pregnancy in 1981 is, in many ways, a less fraught and difficult experience than it was in the past. However, there is much that can still be done to improve the care given to pregnant women.

3 My Way or Theirs? – Giving Birth

Giving birth is the single most important event in most women's lives. Whether the experience is happy and rewarding or tense and frightening can have a profound effect on the ease with which she changes from being pregnant to being a mother.

If the birth is relaxed and the woman feels that it is she who is 'calling the shots' or at the very least having some say in what is being done, that it is *she* who has delivered her baby, then her confidence to take over the care of the child gets a terrific boost.

Women for whom unavoidable problems do arise during labour or delivery need not lose this sense of achievement. If good communication exists between the woman and those attending her, if problems and procedures are explained and choices offered, then women can still feel positively about the birth. The overwhelming sense of relief that all is well with the baby overrides any regrets that the birth was not 'natural'.

However, if the woman does not have confidence in or a liking for her midwife or doctor, if machines and drugs are routinely used without regard to the kind of birth the woman may wish for, then the sense of being responsible for the birth is taken from her. If the midwife does not believe she can manage without drugs, the woman may feel she was wrong to think she could. If the doctor rules that an episiotomy must be performed routinely, then a woman's will to deliver her baby in her way is eroded.

Every woman has her own idea of a happy birth. For some, to have a natural, drug-free birth is not the most important thing. For such women, to have a pain-free birth is more important. As many women complained that drugs were not available when expected (especially epidurals), as complained that they were given drugs against their wishes.

For others, to experience the full force of birth is vital. A woman who understands what is happening to her body and has attendants who have confidence in her ability to do it 'herself' may wish to be fully aware of the miracle of birth. The happiest descriptions of labour and delivery came from women who were given the choice as to how and where they gave birth.

Overriding even the importance of choice is the tremendous gratitude which women feel for the person, whether midwife or doctor, who treats them with kindness and reassurance during labour and delivery. Almost 90 per cent said they found the medical staff 'mostly helpful and sympathetic'. The midwife 'comes into her own' once labour has started. No woman said 'who was the midwife?' or 'never saw one' when describing the birth. As we have seen, this was quite common in the antenatal period. It was the midwife who was solely in charge of over half of the deliveries and it is she who underlies much of the satisfaction expressed by women about their deliveries.

A happy birth and a safe one?

For a baby, the journey from the womb to the outside world can be a dangerous and difficult one. Indeed, about 1.3 per cent of 1981 babies died at or around the time of birth. However, 'being born' is getting safer all the time. Ten years ago over 2.4 per cent of babies died. In 1958 the number was even higher, at 3.3 per cent.*

There are many factors explaining why a baby's chance of surviving pregnancy and birth are higher today than they have ever been: the improving health of women, more widely available contraception and abortion facilities, and better screening for the congenital abnormalities which usually result in the death of the baby.

* This figure comes from the 1958 survey: Butler, N.R. and Bonham, D.G. *Perinatal motality. The first report of the 1958 British Perinatal Mortality Survey* (Livingstone 1963).

More skilled obstetric and paediatric care has also contributed to the improving health of new babies. Better monitoring during labour gives a more accurate indication of how a stressed baby is standing up to delivery than did more traditional methods. More sophisticated care of the very sick or very small new-born baby has helped to save babies who were previously at risk of death and handicap. Many women wrote to us expressing their overwhelming relief that their baby was healthy following unexpected distress, placental failure, high blood pressure or a premature birth. These women had no hesitation in praising the hospitals and all their expertise and technology.

Seventy-nine per cent of women reported no serious problems arising during birth for the baby. Roughly two thirds of labours and deliveries progressed with no problems occurring to either woman or baby. Can hospitals (90 per cent of deliveries took place in consultant units) provide a relaxed and non-clinical birth with familiar staff, and a quick return home if wanted for those women who are unlikely to develop problems? If choice in *how* to give birth is not available in hospitals, women may increasingly opt out of hospital care, choosing to give birth in their own way. If hospitals can rise to this challenge, and some already seem to, then many more women will feel they do not have to make a choice between a regimented but safe birth, or a relaxed birth away from expert help should it be required.

The place of birth

Ten years ago 66 per cent of births took place in a consultant unit. Our survey suggests that this figure has risen significantly, to around 90 per cent. The number of women delivered by their GP or local midwife in a GP unit has fallen from 18 per cent in 1970 to 7 per cent in our survey. Those women delivering at home fell from 12 per cent to 2 per cent.

If present trends continue, delivery at home or in a GP unit could become something of a rarity. Given the high degree of satisfaction expressed by women about such deliveries, their phasing-out could be regrettable and would certainly lead to the virtual elimination of choice for women as to where they give birth. If women likely to develop problems can be skilfully selected for consultant delivery, and women who develop last-minute difficulties can be easily transferred, risk to mother and baby can be greatly reduced.

Many women reported on transfers either during pregnancy or even after labour had begun, and they appeared to work efficiently.

Getting to hospital

Most women travelled to the hospital with their husbands, by car, to have their baby. Some went by ambulance, especially when labour was advanced, while others who were booked in for an induction even went by public transport. Some of the happiest journeys were when the community midwife drove the woman and her husband to hospital where she was to do the delivery. This often enabled much of the first stage of labour to progress at home. Other women went to hospital for an antenatal check and were surprised to discover that a transfer to the labour ward was advised!

These are some typical and not-so-typical accounts of the journey to hospital. **Janet**, from Eastbourne, is an accounts clerk:

> *My waters broke at 7.45 p.m. on 28 May 1981. My husband rang the hospital and they advised me to go in straight away. My husband took me to the hospital in the car. I reckon husbands should have relaxation classes – he thought he was a racing driver, going around Brands Hatch – well, he drove like it, anyway.*

Anne, from Bridgend, found she had to wait for her husband to come home because her hospital was in the wrong area for the ambulance. She is a household management executive:

> *I started contracting every two to three minutes immediately and telephoned my husband to collect me. He arrived within an hour. I could not telephone for an ambulance, as I live in Mid Glamorgan and my hospital was in South Glamorgan, twenty miles away. They will not cross the borders.*

Margaret, from Alton, had an unexpected start to her labour:

> *I went to Portsmouth hospital by ambulance at 5 a.m. on 25 May after my waters broke at 4 a.m. We were on holiday at the time in Hayling Island, our first night in a caravan on a*

waterlogged caravan site. I paddled to the ambulance in my black welly boots and plastic mac through 3 inches of water and mud, hanging grimly on to the arm of a friendly ambulanceman. Arrived at the hospital at 5.30 a.m. and Louise Ann arrived at 5.45 a.m.

Lynda's story was a typical account of how the domino scheme can provide continuity of care from home to hospital. She lives in Rochester:

At 9.00 a.m. I phoned my local midwife (attached to my own doctor) who came to examine me and (10.00 a.m.) decided to take me in straight away (10.30 a.m.) in her own car. The baby was born two hours later, with the same midwife and a student in attendance.

Some women even managed to go shopping in the early stages of labour! **Jana**, from Salisbury, is a clerical officer:

The two days previous to Katy being born, I had suffered very slight discomfort from backache, but nothing to cause any great alarm. I was due at the hospital clinic at 11.30 on the Thursday morning. I went into town first and while walking around Marks and Spencers I felt as if I was carrying the shopping between my legs. On arriving at the clinic, I said that I felt uncomfortable, but nothing too bad. The doctor examined me internally and began to laugh, as did the midwife. I asked to be let in on the joke and the doctor asked me if I would like to have the baby that day, as my cervix was nearly eight centimetres dilated. We all laughed and I was taken straight to the labour ward. That was 12.30; Katy arrived at 3.15 p.m.

Some women found getting admitted to the labour ward was not so easy. Several women commented on the problems they had in persuading the sister on duty that labour was well established. This seemed more of a problem when the night staff was on duty. **Jane**, from Tonbridge, is a teacher:

I was admitted to hospital around 2 a.m. on my own insistence, because of the severity of the pains, after two phone calls during which sister on duty tried to persuade me not to bother. She suggested I took some Panadol and went to bed with a hot water bottle! If that had been all I needed I would scarcely have been on the phone asking to be admitted. I knew that I was in labour, but I had great difficulty in persuading her that I knew what was happening and that I needed to be in hospital. My husband drove me in our own car, a painful twenty-minute journey.

First impressions

Women were not always made to feel welcome on arrival at the labour ward. A friendly word from Sister, or whoever is the first member of staff to be seen, can affect a woman's whole feeling about the forthcoming delivery, particularly if she is nervous anyway. First impressions are important. One golden rule seems to be – try not to arrive when the shift is changing! **Carol**, from Catford in London, wrote:

I unfortunately arrived at the hospital when the staff were changing shifts. I was left alone and given no pain-killers at all, not even gas/air.

Kirsty did not enjoy her arrival at the hospital:

On arrival I was made to feel most unwelcome (except by the doctor), as the staff had been very busy and I arrived just when they thought they were going to have a rest. I was asked my views on painkillers and the midwife was angry when I said I wanted to see how I could go without. (As it happened it wasn't very long.) She argued with the doctor about it.

Anita, from Leeds, is a sales assistant. She told us:

When I got to the hospital a midwife took me into a room where she did all the necessary preparations. She then took me to the delivery room, where I was left for fifteen minutes alone. She came back in and said she was going to give me an injection of pethidine. I said I didn't want one and that I just wanted my husband, who had been sat outside.

These stories point to the importance of a smooth introduction into the hospital, but also the the need for communication between the woman and the staff attending her. Kirsty and Anita wanted no pethidine and felt pressured to have it, while Carol was hoping for some pain relief and received none. But more on drugs later in this chapter.

Big hospitals, small units or home?

Big hospitals Some impressions, good and bad, of consultant hospital deliveries follow. It is encouraging that there were so many cheerful and happy stories about consultant units. This shows that a big unit does not necessarily have to mean a clinical and impersonal touch. In fact, some of the most sophisticated and technological hospitals in the country produced some of the most touching stories about happy births. Do such hospitals find it easier to attract staff who are not only medically expert, but who also have the capacity to relate well to women in labour? The story of happy labours and deliveries is all about people and how they relate to one another.

These descriptions of birth in high technology consultant/university hospitals shows that birth in such places can be a personally rewarding experience. This may be especially so if the woman is knowledgeable and able to express her wishes forcefully. **Julia**, from Cambridge, described the birth of her third child:

> *I had no drugs and no gas and air. The midwife was a friend of my NCT class midwife and let me conduct the labour in the way I wanted. Although Ben was very large (11lb), the labour and delivery was very fulfilling and satisfying. I was allowed to adopt the position I wished (nearly sitting up) . . . the midwife was wonderful, she allowed me to set my own pace and only took over if she felt I was struggling a bit . . . I felt in control of the whole labour and birth, but in the reassuring safety of the hospital (Mill Road Hospital, Cambridge).*

Mary, from Didcot, was one of several women praising the John Radcliffe Hospital, Oxford's handling of a difficult birth:

> *After an internal examination the baby's hand and arm were found to be over the head, so I had an emergency Caesarian section . . . my preparation was superb, everything was explained and great kindness and sympathy shown.*

Linda, from Crediton, appreciated the personal touch in a big hospital:

> *I was very comfortable in labour, with pleasant surroundings and piped music to take my mind off things. My baby arrived to the 'Dying Swan' and Strauss waltzes.*

Katy, from Nottinghamshire, was very satisfied with her consultant hospital delivery:

The midwife, although performing her first delivery on her own, exuded confidence and competence and was most reassuring. She also took the time to answer my questions as best she could.

Although I was in a relatively large maternity unit and aware that sisters and doctors were nearby if required, the delivery was quite private and personal with only the midwife and my husband present. The pethidine seemed to have been given at just the right time for maximum effect when most needed.

Carol, from Southampton, is a telephone sales clerk. She had a difficult birth and found that there was a personal touch even though ten people were present:

At every stage of my labour I and my husband were given all information and allowed to discuss it before deciding. There were ten medical people present at the birth; all were very helpful, calm and patient – we were told all that was happening all the time.

Karen, from Lincolnshire, is twenty. Her second baby (after three miscarriages) was delivered in a small consultant unit:

It was fantastic, no painkillers, completely normal. Labour was quick and the staff were so helpful. My husband was there, it was great. No one should miss the experience.

Susan, from Wrexham, is a postmistress. She was also delivered in a small consultant unit:

Pleasant, cheerful and helpful nurses, atmosphere background music, no bullying.

But, sadly, many consultant deliveries did not work out so well. Women did not feel welcome, procedures such as enemas, shaves, breaking of the membranes and electronic monitoring seemed to be done automatically, without any regard to personal preference.

Another reason for less happy experiences in hospitals was staff shortages and changing shifts. Many women reported that midwives were rushed off their feet, with several deliveries to cope with at once. Others found the change from day shift to night shift resulted in having to establish new relationships, sometimes very close to delivery. Several women reported that day staff were more sympathetic than night staff. With almost half of all women (46 per cent) delivering between 6 p.m. and 6 a.m., a reduced night staff may result in a poorer service for many women.

Sheryl, from Cheshire, describes a consultant unit birth which combines many of the criticisms levelled at the management of birth in some (but fortunately not all) consultant units. The only contact she had with medical staff seems to have been when tests and procedures were being carried out. Perhaps if a midwife had been able to sit with her and her husband, communication would have been better and more attention paid to her feelings:

I was booked into hospital at 9.30 a.m. to be induced. I was taken into a preparation room and given a full pubic shave and an enema, then at 11.00 a.m. I was given a pessary to start contractions, which began almost immediately, but none of the staff came to see how I was doing. They just saw that I was knitting and must have thought that nothing was happening because I wasn't screaming in pain. It wasn't until the change of staff at 5.00 p.m., when the staff nurse came to me and I told her that I was having regular contractions every ten minutes, that she examined me and found I was four centimetres dilated. Then she asked a doctor to examine me and after another hour's wait he said that he would rupture my waters. After my waters had been ruptured I was put on an oxytocin drip and a monitor which wasn't registering my contractions, and the staff did not palpate my contractions at any time – right up to the time I wanted to bear down they just said, 'Oh, no, it's not time yet', without examining me. It wasn't until I really made a fuss that they examined me and found that the baby was coming, so they shouted for the trolley, which I had to jump on to, off the bed, and I was rushed into delivery. The baby only needed two pushes out. They knew I had had another baby before but they still didn't believe I wanted to push.

And **Carol**, from Milton Keynes wrote:

When I was pregnant I got the idea that they would welcome me and make me comfortable, or just be friendly. I felt very lonely and freezing cold the whole time!

Shirley, from York, pinpointed the problems that can arise when staff are under unusual pressure of work:

They were terribly overworked and there was a lady giving birth to twins, which was complicating their usual busy schedule. If it had not been for my husband being with me, I would have given up many times. The fleeting visits from the nurses were certainly not enough and the changeover of night staff halfway through didn't help.

The importance of having one midwife staying beside you through labour and delivery was stressed over and over again. Women in labour need the help and advice of one midwife whom they get to know and trust. The husband or partner is, of course, the other most important companion. Ninety-two per cent of women had their husbands with them during labour and 61 per cent had either their husband or a close friend or relative with them during delivery.

Catherine, a hairdressing lecturer from Blackburn, points to the distress that can be caused to a woman when a hospital fails to arrange things properly with her husband:

I was quite frightened because I was on my own for most of the time. They had told my husband to go, because there was a long time to go before anything would happen. My husband wasn't keen to watch the birth but would have stayed with me beforehand . . . I got the impression that they were busy, and I did not have the midwife stay with me until I was pushing – before that I had to ring the bell if I needed anything . . . I was rather frightened and would have preferred a midwife with me all the time.

Small units and domino deliveries Women were very satisfied with deliveries in so-called 'isolated' GP units. These are geographically apart from the consultant unit and are usually in a small town or village. Women from rural areas felt a particular affection for these units. Unlike their urban counterparts, they provided the only possibility of a hospital delivery near to families and friends. The advantage of familiar staff was also a decisive factor. There was much criticism of the current trend towards closing down the isolated GP units.

An arrangement which came in for much praise was the domino scheme, whereby the advantages of being delivered by the midwife who has cared for you during pregnancy can be offered within the big hospital. The woman is taken to hospital by her local midwife, delivered by her and then returned home a few hours later, where her postnatal care continues under the same midwife. This scheme achieves a measure of continuity of care which is very rewarding both for women and midwives. Domino schemes are popular in city areas, where they operate within the local consultant unit. Where consultant and midwives and GPs have made it possible for such arrangements to develop, women have an option available to them which combines some of the benefits of hospital and home. Where such schemes are not operating the demand for home deliveries is likely to be higher.

Another popular option available in some places is a delivery in a GP unit which is attached to a consultant unit. This can offer the cosiness of a small unit with the proximity of large hospital facilities.

Here are some typical stories of domino and GP unit deliveries. First, isolated GP unit deliveries. **Irena**, from Skegness, had her third baby in a small cottage hospital:

Skegness Hospital is a cottage hospital with a very friendly, personal, 'small is good' atmosphere which was relaxed and intimate. Individual attention given all the time. One felt part of a family. The maternity unit is soon to close due to too few pregnancies to maintain beds. Mothers will have to travel to a large hospital twenty or thirty miles away. This will be a sad loss locally.

Sheilagh, from Northumberland, describes the advantages to her of the isolated GP unit and the personal care it can provide:

I was allowed complete freedom of movement during my

labour. I was allowed to wander around the wards and use the labour ward when I felt the need for peace and quiet. My trust in doctors and midwives grew from strength to strength.

I was frightened when I went into hospital to be induced, but the doctor and midwives put me completely at ease, and I felt at ease during labour and the birth. I had made no arrangements for my husband to be present, but there were no objections when I asked if he could stay . . . As our maternity unit in Alnwick is small, it provides a home-from-home atmosphere. Each patient is an individual and the staff knows which baby belongs to which mother. These types of unit are rare in this country but the need for them is great. A mother needs to feel she is the only person in the country that is giving birth. There is a larger hospital fifteen miles away where mothers are sent if an emergency arises. This gave me great confidence.

I and my husband were left alone a lot of the time, knowing that if we rang the bell a midwife would arrive straight away . . . It was a wonderful experience for both of us . . . Whilst I was in hospital (GP unit) several nurses told us that there had been talk of the hospital closing down as it was not economical to run. We were all concerned about this as we had enjoyed our stay, and we all agreed that it was a great pity as it was the nearest thing to a home confinement, with the back-up of specialist care if it was needed.

Gwendolyn, from St Albans, gives a clear account of her approval of the small units where she had her two babies. She also points out that in a subsequent pregnancy she would opt for a home delivery rather than go to a big hospital:

May I add that 'Red House' GP unit (Harpenden Memorial Hospital) and St Albans City Hospital are small units which are being exposed to threatened closures, probably like many others in many places. But what these people who want to close them cannot see, is that we, the actual mothers, do not wish to go to ghastly cattle-markets with continuous conveyor belts. I can say that smaller units are far more friendly, and the care for each individual is there after you have had the baby. You are known and remembered even after four years . . . Both my births were at St Albans City Hospital. But if these places close, cattle-markets would take over, with such a big turnover I would prefer to have another baby at home, rather than face the attitude of, 'One in, one out, next please, thank you, goodbye. Um! sorry, what's your name?' Let them stay. The smaller units are much better and I know that is the opinion of many.

Susan, from Wallasey, is a bank clerk:

The hospital where I had my baby is soon to close down. Unfortunately, we are all to go to one big central maternity unit and I am sure it will all become rather impersonal.

Susan, from Wokingham, is a computer programmer:

My husband and I were absolutely delighted with the treatment we were both afforded at this GP unit. The delivery was relaxed, with kind and considerate staff, unlike my previous delivery at the consultant unit, where the pressure was absolutely terrifying.

Linda, from Gloucestershire, describes her delivery in a country GP unit:

I was never left alone during labour and usually had the midwife with me. When the baby was about to be delivered, my GP was called from the surgery across the road to deliver the baby and do the stitching-up necessary . . . the birth was the best part as I felt as if I was doing something, and the pain was hardly noticeable. It was also very special that my own GP was called in for the birth, and although everything was normal, it gave a feeling of great security.

Descriptions of deliveries which occurred within the consultant unit but under the care of the GP or community midwife (domino deliveries) were as positive as the stories about deliveries in GP units (isolated or attached).

Barbara, from Pinner, was delivered in a GP unit attached to a large North London consultant unit:

I was delivered by my own GP and a very friendly midwife, which helped enormously. She was a 'motherly' midwife who put me at ease and sat on the bed and chatted to me . . . it was nice that I managed with only gas and air and that I didn't have to have any monitoring equipment . . . I felt in control most of the time and alert once the baby was born.

Janet, from Aylesbury, preferred her third baby's delivery in the GP unit attached to the hospital:

> *In contrast to my previous labours which were in the hospital section, I found the atmosphere much more relaxing and I was not confined to bed until the end of the first stage. I considered it the best possible way for delivery, being relaxed but with the reassurance that expert assistance and technology was available only an elevator ride away, if things did go seriously wrong.*
>
> *I was allowed to do what I wished for recreation during the early part of labour. In fact I watched television with my husband in the TV room until my waters broke. The staff were all friendly and relaxed, but kept careful checks on the progress of labour and kept me informed on how the labour was progressing. This was in marked contrast to my previous labour, which was induced, and where I was confined to bed, and wired up to a drip and monitors which were most uncomfortable.*

Transfers from GP unit care to consultant care do not always meet with approval but may be essential if problems arise in pregnancy or labour. **Carol**, from Redhill, was transferred for antenatal and delivery care from a GP unit to a consultant unit, and felt she had missed out on the kind of delivery she wanted:

> *I would have liked the choice of the Leboyer method, to have known staff better and to have remained within the GP unit. After a complication at thirty-five weeks I was transferred automatically to the consultancy unit, although my GP was keen to retain me in the GP unit.*

Although, as in Carol's case, a transfer may not be welcomed or thought necessary, it is important, if GP units (both inside and outside consultant units) continue and perhaps even expand, that transfers can be made easily when problems do arise. Much anxiety could be avoided if the reasons for transfer are fully discussed with the woman concerned.

Domino deliveries were described, by and large, in glowing terms. **Gillian**, from south-east London:

> *In the hospital delivery suite, you feel relaxed and allowed to do almost as you please. The staff are very friendly and*

helpful. Having a community midwife deliver me was more like being at home.

Close contact with the community midwife is the feature of the domino scheme which distinguishes it from the other schemes described in this section. **Lynda**, from Rochester, wrote:

The personal care of the domino scheme and my own midwife, this time, was a great improvement on last time. I would recommend this scheme to everyone. It is marvellous (if a normal birth is expected, of course). Such good care and attention.

Sally, from Weymouth, is a vet:

I had a hospital delivery because I consider it safest for baby, but under this domino scheme I was able to come home quickly – the ideal compromise between a hospital and a home delivery. My husband and community midwife were with me. They asked if I preferred to do without pethidine (I did) and agreed when I said I'd rather not have an artificial rupture of the membranes (breaking the waters) for the scalp electrode. The waters broke quite late and I was only in the second stage about ten minutes – there was only just time to get to the labour ward. Just a couple of breaths of gas and air – the rest of the time I just coped on breathing techniques.

The actual birth was marvellous and I was allowed to hold and feed the baby immediately. He was very bright and lively (I hadn't realized till looking back on it how dopey my first baby had been). Also, I wasn't disorientated and tired as I was the previous time (due mainly to pethidine), so I felt much more in control.

However, there *were* some problems with domino and GP deliveries. Firstly, a lack of cooperation between hospital staff and community staff could sometimes lead to an unpleasant atmosphere in the labour and delivery room. A woman in labour is especially sensitive to the atmosphere around her and any conflicts or arguments can be very distressing. **Odette** said:

My own GP was marvellous, but the hospital midwife was most obstructive to my GP as she didn't approve of her coming in and interfering, which made my husband and me feel very uncomfortable.

Secondly, a woman who had expected all through her pregnancy to be delivered by her community midwife could feel very disappointed if, for any reason, at the last minute she was not available. **Carol**, from Catford:

My liaison midwife was cancelled without me being informed because they thought there could be problems with the baby.

Thirdly, there was the problem of emergency transfer of women in labour. With expert screening the need for this should be reduced to a minimum, but it can still be necessary. **Jill**, from Halesowen, was expecting her second baby:

I was taken from Mary Stevens Maternity to Wordsley Hospital because of complications during birth. I went by car in the first instance to the maternity home when contractions were regular. As there was a delay in the second stage of labour (due to the baby being 'twisted'), I was taken by ambulance to hospital and had a forceps delivery. It was a very lengthy labour, which I did not anticipate, it being a second baby.

This is, of course, one of the advantages of the GP unit attached to the consultant unit. A woman developing unexpected difficulties can easily be transferred to the specialist unit, usually just down the corridor.

Another type of scheme, involving community staff, which aims to encourage continuity of care between GP and community midwife, was described by **Jacqui**, from West Drayton:

Hillingdon Hospital and the local GP run a scheme which enables the mother to remain in hospital for only a few hours after the birth of her baby. In my case Samuel was born at 12.30 p.m. and I was home again by 3.30 p.m. The mother then receives daily visits from the midwife for ten days. This seems to be the best alternative to a home delivery, which is so difficult to have these days.

It is clear from this section that there are many different schemes working successfully to provide community-based systems of delivery care. These schemes seem to result in a rewarding and happy experience for the woman, while also providing a medical back-up service should something go wrong. There are many areas where these options are not available, where GPs have lost interest in obstetric care, where consultants prefer not to invite community-based staff into their units, or where isolated GP units are closing for reasons of economy. Where these things are happening a woman's choice about how she has her baby is greatly reduced, and becomes quite simply a matter of 'big hospital' or home. For many women the mixture of the two is the perfect alternative.

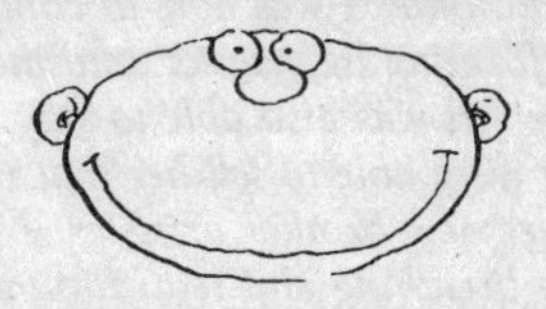

Home sweet home Only 2 per cent of the women in our survey delivered their babies at home, compared with 12 per cent in 1970.* There were also women who would have delivered at home but did not because no service existed, so the figure of 2 per cent is not a true reflection of demand. Home deliveries were, almost without exception, described in the most glowing of terms. There can be little doubt that, for some women, the perfect birth is that which takes place at home where they feel relaxed, loved and above all in control. The first stage was usually easier and the second stage was conducted in a spirit of shared effort and joy which was not so often present outside the home. These are some of the descriptions we had of home births. **Lesley**, from Manchester, had her third baby at home:

> *My labour was a truly delightful experience, in familiar surroundings, attended by professional people that I regarded as friends. We were all truly moved at the birth . . . How unlike hospital!*

Pamela, from Stockton on Tees, had her second baby at home:

> *I felt very relaxed and confident. I washed and set my hair. I had to get the rollers out in a hurry as the first stage progressed quickly! My son was involved by the midwives, whom he had got to know very well. He felt my contractions with the midwife and had all his questions answered. My*

* *British Births 1970* (William Heinemann Medical Books 1975).

husband and mother were with me. A doctor was present, but left everything in the calm and capable hands of the midwives . . . I felt very special. It was marvellous. The second stage was very quick and easy and our daughter was handed to me immediately.

The involvement of other children was very important to women having babies at home. **Celia** from Tamworth said:

As I remained at home, I was able to continue walking around and performing light tasks until the latter stages of labour. My little girl was also able to stay with me until her bedtime and we were able to tell her that when she woke up she would see her new brother or sister. I was able to put into practice the breathing and relaxation exercises I had been taught, with no interference. I felt much more in control than during my previous labour.

The smoother the introduction of a new baby is into the life of an older child, the better he or she is likely to respond to it. When mother is taken away to a strange place to have the baby it takes, perhaps, a greater amount of sensitive handling to integrate the new baby into the family.

Difficult births occurring unexpectedly at home were not common. One of the few reported was well handled by the midwife and damage to the baby avoided. But such stories do point to the risks inherent in home deliveries. If the three minutes of non-breathing of **Maureen's** baby had been longer, it could have been brain-damaged or died:

At the start of labour I telephoned the midwife, who came straight away. Her manner and good humour put me completely at ease and she was with me until 8.30 a.m., when another midwife took over who was equally good with me. I cannot praise the midwives in Bury highly enough . . . the cord was round his neck and was cut and clamped before delivery and he didn't cry for three minutes, but everything turned out all right.

Home birth must be planned and prepared for if it is to turn out as successfully as these births did. However, where a home birth takes place unplanned, a woman's feelings about it are likely to be very different. **Sylvia** said:

I did not enjoy labour. It was very painful due to the fact that I had no painkillers and I was frightened as my husband had to leave me to chat up a friend to phone for an ambulance . . . the baby was born at home, and the midwife advised me to go to hospital for a check-up for me and the baby, to check for internal bleeding because of delivering the baby without help and alone, and because the baby turned blue.

Annette delivered her baby at home in one hour with the help of the ambulance staff:

I had a GP/midwife booking at my local maternity hospital. I started in labour at just after 3 a.m. with a show. Ten minutes later I had my first contraction. After dressing I rang for an ambulance and the community midwife, but whilst on the phone I had a bad contraction with which my waters broke and I wanted to bear down. The ambulance was about ten minutes in arriving, by which time I had to lie down on the settee. As I was about to be moved another contraction came, and the ambulance men realized that the baby's head was there and advised me to push. My baby was born at 4 a.m. I had ripped during the birth, so the ambulance men waited for the midwife to arrive, cut the cord and tidy me up before taking me to the maternity unit.

Annette's choice of a GP unit delivery did not materialize – nature beat her to it. But the message is clear; women want to have a choice as to *where* they give birth as well as *how*. A re-examination of the trend towards closing small units, and not allowing for home deliveries as an option, is vital if women's preferences are to be taken into account. Women feel that they are more likely to be able to give birth 'their way' in a small unit or at home. On the other hand, the more big hospitals can provide for choice and reduce interference to a minimum, the less will be the pressure on women to opt out.

Labour

This section is about labour – that period of time before delivery which for some women lasted less than one hour, while for others it lasted more than twenty-four. What did the survey tell us about women and labour? Did women enjoy labour? Who was with them during labour? How many labours were induced? How many women or their babies were attached to foetal monitors? Was pain relief available when required, or conversely, were drugs used too readily? Were procedures explained? How far were women left wondering what was happening and whether everything was OK? Were women able to use the relaxation techniques they had been taught?

Recent trends

In comparing the management of labour in 1970 with 1958, *British Births 1970* commented on these changes that had taken place:

- greater sophistication of pain-relieving techniques
- greater awareness of the mother's emotional needs
- less likelihood of women being left on their own to endure prolonged labour with its risks of demoralization and of adverse chemical changes.

Since 1970, according to our survey, these trends have continued, although there are still women who complain that they were left alone too much. Six per cent said they were left alone 'most of the time' and nearly 20 per cent 'some of the time'. The tremendous growth in the now common pattern for husband to be present during labour and/or delivery has helped to reduce problems of loneliness during labour but it does still seem that, for whatever reason, some women have less companionship and support during labour than they would like.

The one factor which was always mentioned when a happy labour was described was the *person* who was present during most or all of the labour and delivery. Ideally this included the husband and a midwife.

Since 1970, a new trend that has emerged is the desire by many women to have some choice in various aspects – how many, if any, drugs they have, what position is adopted for labour and delivery, whether an episiotomy is performed or not.

These are questions which, ten years ago, women were perhaps more inclined to leave to the medical staff to decide. The last decade has seen the emergence of a new self-confidence in women, and the desire to keep control during childbirth is one more manifestation of the fundamental changes that are occurring in the position of women in society.

Who enjoys labour?

Most women had mixed feelings about labour. Expressions such as 'Who enjoys pain?', 'it was a means to an end', 'it was hard work but worth it', 'the pain was worth while', were common. In answer to the question, 'Did you enjoy labour?' the majority answered, 'some of the time' (37 per cent). However, 29 per cent answered that they enjoyed labour 'most of the time' and 34 per cent answered 'not at all'. There are no comparable figures from previous surveys but it seems likely that with better pain relief (especially the epidural), plus shorter labours, more women in 1981 can look back happily on their labours than did in the past.

There is no room for complacency, however. Future trends will hopefully see a reinforcement of women's desire for freedom of action and an increasing respect for natural birth, with medical and technological interference kept to a minimum. Here are some typical quotes from women about their labour and induction. This will be followed by comments on pain relief and monitoring.

These women enjoyed their labour – they were given choice, they were attended by midwives they liked and they felt in control of what was going on, very often following good preparation classes. **Susan**, from Port Talbot, told us:

It was easy. I was so alert and knew what to do, the nurses asked me what I wanted to do and even when I wanted my waters broken. I was spoken to as if I really did have a say in it.

Anne, from Bristol, wrote:

My contractions were all in my back and my husband had learnt how to massage my back at the NCT classes. This proved to be very effective and it was a satisfying experience to be able to cope with the labour by our own efforts.

The staff were superb – they let my husband and me use the breathing that we had practised, and no pressure was put on us to conform to any hospital routine. No mention was made of the problem they had discovered with the placenta until the baby was safely delivered, so I remained totally relaxed throughout.

Elizabeth, from Sutherland, said:

I practised my breathing exercises throughout labour and, with the help of my husband, found them extremely helpful in focusing attention away from the contractions. As a result I felt very much in control of the situation and I was totally aware of what was going on all the time.

Women were appreciative of the midwives who discussed what they were doing beforehand. **Margaret**, from Coventry, wrote:

I was treated with consideration and sympathy. On admission the midwife offered to break the waters artificially and I accepted. She also took the trouble to stop her examination during the contractions.

Women were full of praise for their husbands or midwives who helped them to remain in control. **Kerry**, from Newquay, said:

My husband and the nursing staff were excellent. They reminded me of my breathing when I lost the rhythm. They were full of praise and encouragement when I got it right again. They were so good that I managed to have my baby without drugs or gas and air.

The very early stages of labour were enjoyed more by women who were able to remain active and at home or where hospitals allowed for freedom of movement. **Sylvia**, from Exeter, wrote:

My labour was not painful, although I was having good contractions. I was free to get out of bed, to stroll along the corridor, go to the toilet, read or just relax.

Elizabeth, from Bristol:

Because my waters broke first my labour was slow to begin with, so I was encouraged to get up and walk about. I even had a shower. I went to the antenatal ward and chatted to other people and went to the nursery to see the babies. In the afternoon, when the contractions got stronger, I sat in a chair and watched TV with my husband.

Lynn, from Cleveland, had her baby at home:

For half of my labour I did not realize that I was in fact in labour and so carried on with the housework as normal. For the last four hours, with the midwife and my husband present, it was more like a social event, everyone chatting and my son playing with his toys beside me . . . I felt an enormous sense of achievement instead of thinking, 'Thank God that's over.'

Thirty-four per cent of women reported that they did not enjoy labour at all. Many of them felt lonely, others frightened and others 'tied down' by drips and monitors. Many women mentioned the discomfort involved in being moved from labour to delivery room, often during the uncomfortable transitional stage between labour and delivery. Lack of choice about position during labour was reported by a surprising 41 per cent of women, whereas only 17 per cent mentioned lack of choice in the use of painkillers. The pleasure which was apparent in the stories just quoted, where women felt free to do as they pleased in labour, reinforces the survey finding that women do care very much about controlling labour and find this much easier to do given freedom of choice.

A further factor which caused distress in labour was lack of preparation. Those women who could not attend or had not attended classes were more likely to suffer from fear and 'losing control' than better-prepared women. Another problem was the feeling of failure which affected women who had 'prepared' but where the birth had not worked out as they had expected it to.

Sheila lives in south-west London. She summed up her labour this way:

Undignified, painful, boring, depressing . . . I hated every minute.

The importance of feeling in control was mentioned by **Linda**, from Newport Pagnell:

I did not seem to have so much control over this birth as I had with my first. I therefore did not find it as enjoyable as the first.

The feeling of failure which can arise when 'natural childbirth' does not 'work' was described by **Catriona**, from Cumbria:

Nothing I had read or heard had prepared me for the fact that regardless of breathing, relaxation, etc., labour was going to hurt and hurt a lot. Consequently I felt I was making a mess of relaxation and felt I had failed . . . I feel I would have enjoyed it much more if I had been better prepared mentally for the pain.

Julia, from Basingstoke, also found that classes had not prepared her for the restrictions imposed on her in hospital:

It was extremely boring as I had been led to believe from antenatal classes that at least I would be able to walk about. Instead I was confined to bed with a drip one side and a foetal heart monitor connected to the baby's head the other side . . . at times during labour the midwife was helpful and sympathetic but only if we did it all her way.

Maureen, from Darlington, commented:

I didn't feel in control of the situation, and although the staff and my husband were there I still felt frightened and unsure.

Perhaps the most important causes of complaint were induction, monitoring, and to a lesser extent, drugs. Also, as we have seen, 41 per cent of women did not feel they had 'reasonable freedom of choice' about position during labour. This percentage rises to 57 per cent when women were asked about position during delivery. **Elaine**, from Solihull, is a teacher:

I feel that I would have enjoyed labour more if I had been given more choice as to the position I lay in.

Maureen, from Darlington, wrote:

I felt much more comfortable on my side but the staff insisted I must lie on my back and I'm sure this made my labour longer and more painful.

Susan, from Derbyshire:

I found the position I was lying in most uncomfortable. I kept being sick, and found the process of being humped on and off trolleys and in and out of bed every time I was examined absolutely exhausting.

Susannah, from Belsize Park, London, is a primary school teacher:

I enjoyed the moment of birth but none of the labour because the position was so uncomfortable, on my side on a high narrow bed, with nothing to push my feet against.

Induction

There were two reasons why induction (or artificial onset of labour) and acceleration (speeding-up labour) became popular during the sixties and seventies. Firstly, the 1958 birth survey showed that pregnancies lasting longer than forty-two weeks were associated with a higher death rate among babies. Secondly, it was thought that obstetric care might be of a higher standard in the daytime and on weekdays than at night or at the weekend.

Another factor was the desire to reduce the length of labour. The 1958 survey had shown that labours of first-time mothers lasting longer than twenty-four hours were associated with higher death rates for the babies than when labour lasted between twelve and twenty-four hours.

By 1970, as many as 26 per cent of all births were induced and 1.5 per cent accelerated. During the seventies induction rates continued to rise to levels as high as 40 per cent in some places.

The results of our survey suggest that the rate of inductions has come down from the mid-seventies peak of 40 per cent. In our survey 34 per cent of labours were induced, showing that rates are still above the 1970 rate of 26 per cent. The decline in the popularity of induction follows public and professional disquiet at its routine use. With uncertainty about dates some babies were being induced prematurely. Others claimed that induction was being used as a way of ensuring that births occurred at a time most convenient to the medical staff – namely on weekdays – and not because there were medical reason for a 'weekday birth'.

Added to this was criticism by women of the discomfort associated with being attached to a drip (through which the drug oxytocin is administered) throughout labour. Other women felt that contractions following induction were unnaturally strong and more difficult to control.

Our survey did not inquire about how inductions were performed. However, the 1970 survey showed that about 45 per cent of inductions were done by artificial rupture of the membrane (ARM), that is, breaking the waters; about 25 per cent by a combination of ARM and an oxytocin drip, and about 12 per cent by an oxytocin drip alone. The remaining inductions were done by various other methods.

Nearly 80 per cent of women in our survey believed that 'medical grounds' were the reason for induction and only 4 per cent gave reasons of 'medical convenience'. Ten per cent of women said they were induced because of their 'own wish'. Five per cent said they did not know why they were induced.

What are the medical indications for an induction? The three main reasons quoted in *British Births 1970* are hypertension (high blood pressure), postmaturity (baby overdue) and cessation of intra-uterine growth (baby is not growing).

Comments from women on induced birth were mostly critical. They disliked being attached to a drip and they found contractions too strong. Breaking of the waters before the onset of labour was found to be painful. It is to be hoped, as more natural and convenient methods are found to start and speed up labour, that the shortcomings of present methods will be reduced. Women, on the whole, are happy to be induced if there is a really good reason for it and if it is fully explained, but a difficult and painful induction may make them less happy to be induced next time. **Susan** is a bank clerk from Wallasey:

Induced labour became very violent very quickly, and I hung on to gas and air like grim death.

Jill is a bank clerk, from Stockwell. She felt her induction was unnecessary as she was already in early labour:

Even though I started myself, I was taken in as though I was to be induced. Therefore I had my waters broken and was connected to monitors and so was unable to walk about. I found it very uncomfortable lying on my side for approximately nine hours!

Lavinia also felt that the induction was unnecessary, and that a forceps delivery resulted from a too-quick labour:

The nurses and medical team were excellent, but my problems could have been caused by their deciding to induce me and it all happening too suddenly. I was only five days overdue and my high blood pressure returned to normal after two hours' bed rest at the hospital, but they still induced!

As I've said, could all this have been avoided by not deciding to induce? My birth experience was a green cloth over my thighs, and my baby being dropped out by forceps while I was held on to at the shoulders. It was like a chicken being gutted – how can that be enjoyed?

Patricia, from Manchester, felt that problems for her and the baby resulted from not being 'left alone':

After coming round from the anaesthetic for exploratory procedure to investigate placenta praevia (none to speak of), I was put on a drip which was switched up at frequent intervals to 'get some action here'. After four to five hours I was told that my baby was distressed and I was only two centimetres dilated. I believe this was because I was induced when my cervix wasn't ready.

My baby was distressed because the waters had been broken early. He was posterior and the head was not engaged, and contractions were strong and frequent due to the oxytocin drip with no prospect of an early vaginal delivery.

They were helpful and sympathetic, but they could not allay my underlying feeling that the baby's distress and Caesarean section could have been avoided if I'd been left alone.

Michelle is nineteen, from Atherton, Lancashire. She is a machinist. It seems that in her hospital one day a week is reserved for inductions:

I was taken in beforehand because of high blood pressure, and then they decided to induce me on the Monday, because that's their inducing day.

Belinda, from Gosport, expressed the feeling of being cheated of a normal birth that some women experience after an induction – especially when they do not feel it was really necessary:

I was ready for the birth and looking forward to having a reasonably relaxed labour and the minimum amount of medical interference. But because I was a bit overdue (nine days) they took away the most important part of pregnancy from me. It took several weeks to come to terms with the induction, and I still feel cheated four weeks after the birth.

The distress that can be caused when doctors do not explain fully why an induction is to be done, is described by **Angela**, who is nineteen years old:

I wasn't given any reason why I was to be induced. The doctor just came on his rounds, looked at my file, and said to the sister, 'yes, if Mrs P. hasn't started by Tuesday we'll start her off and have her upstairs.' Then he looked at me and said, 'OK?' What could I say? I was terrified and couldn't stop crying when my husband came to visit me.

Some women reported problems in getting the drip attached properly. **Ann**, from Cheshire, said:

The doctor who induced me had five attempts to put the drip in and got annoyed with me for having a tough skin.

Complaints were made about the restriction of movement involved in being attached to an oxytocin drip. **Fiona**, from Bradford, wrote:

My labour would not have been so bad but for the monitor machine straps and the drip. Every time I had a pain I couldn't move because I was fastened both sides by thongs. The drip kept coming undone and bleeding if I put my weight on it.

Some women, as we have seen, were happy to be induced and

even asked to be (10 per cent). Others were able to move around their beds even when attached to the drip.

Jean, from Mitcham, was fourteen days overdue when she was induced, but:

I was perfectly happy to have the induction as I was feeling tired, and despondent of the baby ever arriving.

Monitoring

An increasing trend since the 1970 survey* has been the explosion in electronic techniques to monitor the heart-rate of the baby during labour and delivery.

The aim of an electronic foetal monitoring device, or indeed any monitoring of the baby before birth, is to pick up immediately any sign of foetal distress so that if necessary the baby can be delivered rapidly – either by Caesarean section, forceps, or vacuum extraction. In theory, this should reduce to a minimum the numbers of babies suffering from shortage of oxygen (anoxia) during birth. Anoxia can be a cause of brain damage leading to the death or handicapping of the baby.

In our survey, over 90 per cent of women said that their baby's heart was monitored during labour or delivery. Electronic monitoring devices were used in as many as 61 per cent of all cases where monitoring was carried out. The remaining women were monitored by the traditional 'trumpet method', whereby the midwife or doctor listens at regular intervals to the baby's heart through an 'ear trumpet' on the woman's abdomen.

Where electronic foetal monitoring was used, it was clear that a tremendous expansion has taken place in the use of the scalp monitor – a device which has only been in use in obstetric units for ten to fifteen years.

Women's comments on foetal heart monitors were mixed. Many women did reinforce the unpopular public image which now surrounds foetal heart monitors, and the scalp monitor in particular. It is difficult to attach, it is painful while being attached, and once attached it greatly restricts freedom of movement. A further comment was made about the efficiency of the device. Much discussion amongst staff interpreting the print-out seemed to take place, and disagreements over interpretation

* See footnote, page 87.

were common. Some women wondered how much reliance could be placed on these machines, when they seemed to fall off with great ease, and when the machine itself often seemed to be faulty.

Other women, though not as many as might have been expected, mentioned the temptation for staff to become 'machine watchers' and to forget about the person who was actually giving birth.

In contrast to these comments were some positive reports from women who felt reassured that the baby's progress was being 'expertly checked'. Reports also came from women who had used a remote control device which enabled them to be monitored while still wandering around the labour ward.

Frances, from Redditch, said:

> *I enjoyed watching the monitoring system and being reassured that the baby was not in distress, and seeing how long and how great my contractions were before delivery.*

Janet, from Carnforth in Lancashire, is a teacher:

> *I was pleased being able to watch a machine which monitored the baby's heartbeat and my contractions. It gave me something to look at and to occupy my mind with. The baby wasn't born until 8.15 p.m., so I was lying in bed, wired to the machine and on a drip for about ten hours. Apart from the labour pains, I felt very bedsore by the end of the day.*

Sharon, from Wood Vale in London, described a new device which may have a great future. It certainly seems that in her case good monitoring did pick up a potential problem:

> *UCH have a marvellous gadget which allows the woman complete mobility – it has a transmitter which you can carry; you can go to the loo, and remain walking or standing throughout labour.*

Her baby did develop:

foetal distress – the heartbeat dropped radically about half an hour before delivery. I was put on pure oxygen and the heartbeat recovered, but the baby was delivered by forceps as little progress was made after half an hour of attempts at normal delivery. There were no delivery problems, and the baby was healthy and breathed spontaneously.

Judith, from Leeds, expressed clearly the mixed feelings that many women have about electronic monitoring:

I would have preferred to walk about and stand during labour, but recognize that foetal and contraction monitoring (and therefore lying still) is part of hospital technology for safer births – I would rather have this and a healthy baby than absolute freedom and no baby at all.

Women who disliked foetal heart monitors often did so because they found them restricting. **Jean** is from Stroud in Gloucestershire:

The midwife was lovely but I was wired up to a machine to test baby's heartbeat and my contractions, and was also on a drip as I was showing signs of sugar in my urine. It was very uncomfortable.

Joyce, from Hounslow, found the monitor required her to remain very still:

I had to be in a lying-down position due to the belt monitor on my tummy. If I moved slightly the baby's heartbeat was lost; consequently I tended to become very stiff and sore, in one position all the time.

Amanda, from Withington, Lancashire, is an operations analyst:

I had to be down all the time because of the drip and internal monitor. I found this very uncomfortable – I often had the urge to squat on all fours but couldn't.

Hilary, from Camborne in Cornwall, wrote:

I prefer to stand during labour so it isn't so painful, but I had to stay in bed because of the heart monitor and a tube which measured the strength of contractions.

The reports that follow are from women who said the machines were not working properly or were difficult to attach. **Ruth**, from Kent, wrote:

The foetal monitor was not connected well and kept coming loose – so the baby's heartbeat appeared to stop many times. The monitor for my contractions was wrongly positioned, therefore it registered very small contractions, so the midwife turned up the rate of the drip for induction several times. When a second midwife came and moved the monitor the contractions were in fact very strong.

Pamela is a bank clerk from Cwmbran, Gwent:

The only thing I didn't like was having the scalp electrode put on the baby's head. It kept coming off and it was painful to have it put back on again. In all, this happened five times before they gave up and put a monitor on my tummy . . . most of the medical people talked to each other as if I wasn't there.

Janice, from Leeds, also found the discussions which went on about what the monitor meant upsetting:

I found it very depressing when the doctors were discussing the baby's heartbeat with the sister in front of me. The sister got quite stroppy with the doctor as she felt things were going well, and all this distraction made me lose concentration . . . I had to lie slightly on to one side with having the scalp monitor. I was told not to lie flat on my back.

It is clear that electronic foetal monitoring has not met with widespread approval. Perhaps with the development of less restricting devices, which also work reliably, some of this criticism will lessen. But there will still be women who will resent the 'interference' involved both for her and her baby in having a clip attached to the baby's scalp or a belt round her tummy. Meanwhile, with 21 per cent of all babies, according to the mothers in our survey, developing 'serious' problems during labour or delivery, the need for conscientious and expert monitoring of the baby's well-being is apparent.

Drugs and painkillers

No drugs? Perhaps the most surprising finding on the use of painkillers in our survey was the number of women who said they gave birth without the use of any drugs. Fifteen per cent of all women answered, 'No' to the question, 'Did you have any painkillers during labour and/or delivery?' This compares with less than 3 per cent in *British Births 1970*. It also shows a reversal of the continuous trend between 1946, when 62 per cent had no analgesia, and 1970. Clearly the natural childbirth movement has done much to encourage and enable women to give birth without drugs or painkillers. It is probable, however, that more better-off women try to have drug-free labours and deliveries. With the preponderance of such women in our survey, it is likely that overall in 1981, fewer than 15 per cent of women actually gave birth without drugs.

Many women who gave birth without drugs reported on the struggle they had to achieve this. Too great an enthusiasm by medical staff to administer drugs rather than lend appropriate support and companionship met with plenty of comment. **Sandra**, from Plymouth, said:

> *I believe childbirth to be the most natural thing in the world and I asked* not *to be given any drugs unless I really needed them, while in labour. I found it much better for me personally, although the nurses tried to persuade me to have pethidine . . . I found this to be more relaxing and natural than being literally doped up to the eyeballs and not knowing what's going on around you.*

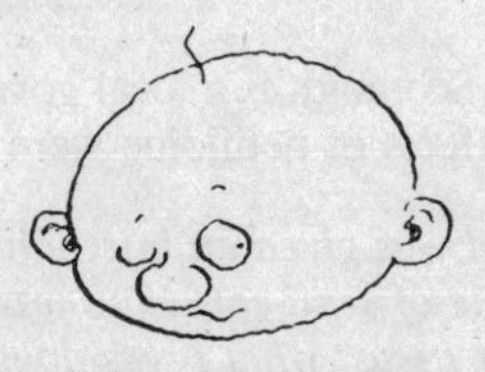

Pethidine and gas and air Out of the women who had painkillers during labour and delivery, 50 per cent had pethidine. This is an underestimate, since our survey did not allow for women who were given pethidine in addition to either an epidural or a general anaesthetic. However, it seems fair to assume that with the increase in women using no pain relief (15 per cent) and those having an epidural (16 per cent in our survey), since 1970 the use of pethidine has been on the decline.

How effective were the painkillers given to women? It is disappointing that 10 per cent of all women said that painkillers were 'not at all effective' and 42 per cent said they were only 'slightly effective'. Some reports suggested that pethidine made women sleepy without dulling the pain, so it is likely that those women who did not find pain relief effective were mainly pethidine and gas and air users.

Certainly pethidine did not meet with great approval. **Penelope**, from Jesmond, Newcastle, pointed to the importance of being given it at the right time:

When the contractions were very strong and I was getting the urge to bear down I asked for pain relief, wanting gas and air. But without examining me I was given pethidine which worried me as I knew the baby's birth was imminent and I was afraid it would depress her breathing.

Laura, from Northumberland, commented:

The midwife kept asking me to have the pethidine but I said I was managing fine, and she said it only lasted for four hours so I thought I had better have it. I was given it at 2.20 p.m. and had the baby at 4.15 p.m. The baby was given an injection to counteract the pethidine. If I had known there was only two hours to go, I would not have had the pethidine.

Helen, from Ayr in Scotland, is a local government officer. Her comments on the effects of pethidine were typical of many:

I was induced and was given an injection of pethidine, which sent me into a state of semi-consciousness. This made me unaware of where I was, what I was doing etc. The treasured moment when the baby arrived was lost as I was unconscious and only remember little bits of the whole labour. I would never *have pethidine again. That mixed with gas and air made me very sick both before my baby was actually born and afterwards. I was unconscious for about three hours afterwards.*

And the effect that drugs can have on control is described by **Angela**, a teacher from Fareham:

The early part of my labour I felt in control and quite happy, but as my labour progressed and I had to have first pethidine and then an epidural because of blood pressure problems I began to feel I was losing control of it and became less happy as time progressed.

Shirley, from Macclesfield, is a self-employed beautician. She gave an account of the not so good effects of pethidine:

Pethidine and gas and air gave me too woozy a feeling. I felt out of control.

I was uncomfortable on the delivery bed and felt very detached. I seemed to keep nodding off and I had really forgotten I was having a baby.

Christine is from West Yorkshire. For her, pethidine was given at the right time so that its effects had worn off in time for her to control the delivery.

I found the birth tiring and hard work but very quick. The effect of the pethidine had worn off by the time the delivery took place and I felt all that was happening and could control the situation.

Several women complained that gas and air made them feel sick. **Laura**, from Glasgow, is a dental surgery assistant. She had rather a different response to pethidine and gas and air:

The only thing I enjoyed about labour was the effect of pethidine and gas and air!

Epidurals There has been a tremendous expansion in the use of epidurals* both for pain relief in normal deliveries and for Caesarian sections. In 1970 0.9 per cent of women had an epi-

* A spinal injection which anaesthetizes the lower half of the body.

dural. Eleven years later according to our survey this has risen to 16 per cent. Roughly 12 per cent of all women had epidurals for vaginal deliveries (forceps included) and 4 per cent had epidurals for Caesarian sections. Women who had Caesarians with a general anaesthetic constituted 6 per cent of the survey.

So epidurals have seen a great growth in popularity during the last ten years. What comments have women made about them? There seem to be three main problems associated with epidurals.

Firstly women felt very cheated when an epidural had been expected and was not available or took a long time to arrive. This tended to happen at weekends or nights when anaesthetists were not so readily available, if at all. Conversely, some women felt pressured into having an epidural when they preferred to 'go it alone'. Finally, women felt rather restricted in their movement because of the epidural needle in their back. Another problem mentioned by some women was the shock of sudden contractions when the epidural had worn off and was due to be topped up.

In contrast to these comments were many women's favourable reports on epidurals – especially where it was combined with a Caesarian. This seems to be a major step forward for women. Many women can now experience that moment when the baby is born by Caesarian section and cries for the first time, whereas before epidurals they could not have done so. Judging by women's comments the Caesarian with epidural has brought an unforgettable moment of joy to many women for which they are very grateful. In addition to being aware of the birth they do not feel sleepy and sick with the after effects of a general anaesthetic. It is worth noting here that it is only in the consultant unit and perhaps some attached GP units that epidurals can be given. This is because an anaesthetist is required to supervise its administration.

Here are some comments – good and not so good – on epidurals. Firstly, some critical remarks about the non availability of epidurals. **Diana**, from Swindon, is a teacher:

I think they tried their best to be kind to me but I was just in so much pain all I wanted was to be put out of my misery. I was told afterwards they could not give me an epidural because there was no one to administer it.

Patricia, from Wigan, is a chemistry teacher. She described her labour as:

Too prolonged and painful. I wanted an epidural but with the birth taking place on a bank holiday an anaesthetist was not available.

Joan, from Bristol, felt cheated of the pain-free labour she had looked forward to:

When pregnant, my own GP promised I would be given an epidural, because I'd had such a bad labour with my first child. On arrival in hospital, I was refused an epidural and refused pethidine (I begged for both). I was given gas and air. One nurse told me to shut up because I was screaming with pain.

I was looking forward to a pain-free labour because my first baby was breech and a very long and painful labour. When an epidural or pethidine were refused me I panicked. It spoilt the whole labour for me.

Joan, from Nottingham, is a clerk. She found it difficult to convince the medical staff that she really was in labour and ready for an epidural:

Another doctor walked in and said 'Do you want an epidural?' I said I'd have anything just to get rid of the pain. By the time the anaesthetist got round to me I was ready to give birth. I gave birth at four o'clock, with a few gasps of gas and air and none of the painkillers I'd asked for. Also they didn't monitor my contractions so they had no idea how strong they were. When my waters broke they said: 'You really are in labour.'

Unlike the women just quoted **Jean**, from Mitcham, felt that she was under pressure to have an epidural:

I found, in general, the staff were helpful; however I felt constantly pressurized to have an epidural which I did not want and my refusal seemed to cause concern. There was no medical reason for an epidural and I considered it unnecessary.

Jacqueline, from Weymouth, is a psychotherapist. She found the epidural affected her capacity to push the baby out:

I found it extremely difficult to push as I was in the lithotomy position [legs up in the air] and due to the epidural I could not feel the contractions. I had to push on verbal command.

Janet, from Darlington, found the epidural prevented her from adopting a comfortable position for delivery, and forceps had to be used. Epidural deliveries are more likely to require forceps because the woman can't feel the contractions and is therefore less likely to push effectively:

After my epidural I felt I wanted to push my baby out from a squatting position – but was told this was not permissible. I did try this – as we were left alone for quite long periods – and the baby did move slightly along the birth canal. It didn't move at all from a lying position – but forceps were eventually needed anyway.

Susan, from Derbyshire, found the epidural very restricting when it came to being moved to the delivery room:

I was examined at regular intervals, but because of the epidural I couldn't climb on and off trolleys, etc. The poor little nurse couldn't manage and had to call a doctor to help (he never looked very pleased about it). Surely there must be a better way than being transferred to a trolley, then into another bed in another room.

Margaret, from Newcastle, found the contractions felt too strong when the epidural wore off:

The epidural was fitted (which took rather a long time). Labour was OK when the epidural was topped up – but a bit of a shock to the system when strong pains came every minute after you hadn't been feeling too much pain.

Barbara, from Farnham, had a very long labour (sixteen hours) and found the epidural did not remain effective throughout. However, she was glad to be able to feel the urge to push:

For the first ten hours the epidural was effective – unfortunately for the last six hours it ceased to be effective, and my tiredness began to take its toll. This was fortunate, I think, in as much as I was able to feel the urge to push and pushed my baby out without the need for medical help which, in retrospect, was very satisfying because I had had so much medical interference up until then.

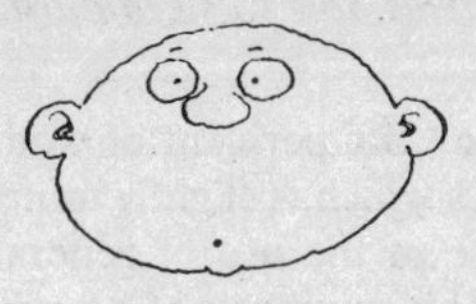

Apart from the reservations experienced above, epidurals were widely appreciated. Some selected quotes follow which express well the almost miraculous experience of being awake while having a Caesarian. **Kathleen** is from Hull:

It was the most fantastic thing that ever happened. I had a general anaesthetic the first time and didn't see the baby until he was five hours old. This time I saw my baby being born and was able to hold her straight away. Thank goodness someone invented the epidural.

Yvonne is from Watford and also preferred her epidural Caesarian to her previous Caesarian:

I had to have a Caesarian section as I have a small pelvis. (This is the second section.) This time I had the operation under an epidural and even though I was afraid to begin with I thought the experience was fantastic and being able to see and hear my son straight away and carry him down to the ward made up for everything.

Marianne, from Edinburgh, is a teacher. This was her third Caesarian but the first one with an epidural:

This was a wonderful experience especially as I had missed the births of my first two children. I can hardly describe the thrill of being able to stay conscious and watch my baby being lifted screaming out of my tummy and then to hold him while being stitched together again. I would recommend this sort of Caesarian to those, like me, who are unfortunate enough always to need one.

Andrea, from Bedfordshire, had an epidural for a normal birth. It was given when she wanted it and relieved her of a painful labour:

Natural childbirth began to prove unbearable for me so I had an epidural. Labour was much easier. I hardly felt the contractions and was able to sleep during them.

General anaesthetic Six per cent of women in our survey had general anaesthetics which is slightly more than in 1970 (5.6 per cent). This increase in the use of general anaesthetics is a reflection of the greater number of Caesarian sections now being done. In 1958 2.7 per cent of women had Caesarians, by 1970 this had risen to 4.5 per cent and according to our survey the rate has now risen to 10 per cent. However the increasing use of epidurals for Caesarians (almost half of Caesarians in our survey were done with epidurals) is reducing the need for general anaesthetic.

Women who have Caesarians under general anaesthetics are less likely to comment on the experience – for obvious reasons – than those who have epidural Caesarians. However, several women mentioned the kindness of the anaesthetist in preparing them for the anaesthetic, and others expressed a sense of relief that they were going to be 'put out of their misery'. Those who commented adversely pointed to the fact that husbands were excluded. One of the great bonuses of the epidural Caesarian is that the husband is usually allowed to be present. Other women mentioned the lack of contact that they felt for the baby – 'I did not feel that it was my baby'. Another disadvantage of the general anaesthetic is the after-effects of the anaesthetic. A feeling of drowsiness and nausea for the day following the operation can also affect the way in which a woman bonds with her new baby. It is clear from the above comments that the more epidurals are used for Caesarians the happier women will be.

Anne, from West Lothian, was happy with the way her general anaesthetic was handled. She had a Caesarian delivery because her baby was in a breech position:

I was wheeled into the theatre before being given the anaesthetic (hospital policy) and I was introduced to everyone. (I already knew the majority.) Without exception they made me feel comfortable, especially the anaesthetist who, sitting at my head, was giving me oxygen to breathe, joked and laughed with me and explained that the noise I could hear was my heart being monitored. The doctor who was going to perform the section told me what would happen and how long it would take approximately.

However, Anne's description of the post-operative period contrasts with the epidural Caesarians:

As I was still under the effects of the anaesthetic the baby wasn't brought to me until she was about five hours old and then again at eight hours old.

In Anne's hospital all Caesarian babies where a general anaesthetic has been administered are 'kept in the baby unit for twenty-four hours to let the mother recover from the effects of the anaesthetic'. **Marie**, from Leigh, is a teacher. Her description brings out very clearly the shortcomings of the general anaesthetic Caesarian – from the woman's point of view:

I knew nothing of it. My husband was left outside knowing nothing and I did not hold my baby on recovery until the next day. My husband was sent home after a two-minute chat.

Paula, from West London, is a company director:

A Caesarian under general anaesthetic does not give you the feeling that you have given birth at all. The result is a certain detachment – I wanted to experience the delivery.

It is evident from this last section that the use of painkillers in childbirth is lessening. This seems to be happening as a response to the desire by women, especially those well prepared in pregnancy, to be as fully aware and in control of labour and delivery as possible. However, those women who did wish for and receive pain relief seem less satisfied with the pethidine/gas and air than with epidurals.

Delivery

Changing fashions in the management of delivery have led to three main differences between 1958 and 1970 (according to *British Births 1970*). Firstly, there was a more extensive use of episiotomy.* Secondly, there was a greater use of forceps or vacuum extraction, and thirdly, a greater use of Caesarians. All these trends have continued since 1970 according to our survey findings.

This section will look at *type* of delivery. Episiotomy will be discussed in the next section.

The trend away from 'normal' vaginal delivery has continued as more deliveries have been performed with the aid of forceps or by Caesarian section. In 1958, 88 per cent of all deliveries were 'normal'. By 1970 this had fallen to 83 per cent and according to our survey this percentage has fallen again to 76 per cent.

The reason for this trend towards more intervention in the birth process are various. Obstetricians have been anxious to reduce prolonged labour and delivery with all the stress that this can cause to mother and baby. Better monitoring and screening of the baby's health before labour begins has enabled doctors to choose the best moment for a baby to be born. A baby who is known to be at risk is more likely to be delivered by Caesarian (especially when premature) or to have the length of labour and delivery reduced to a minimum. Electronic foetal monitoring during labour has also probably led to more babies being delivered fast (with forceps and emergency Caesarians) to save them from brain damage due to oxygen shortage. (Some experts argue that electronic monitoring has also prevented the sort of intervention previously occurring in cases where it was difficult to be confident about the baby's state of health.)

There is much argument about reasons for increasing intervention in delivery but, whatever the truth about the 'medical takeover' of birth, few would question the belief that some babies who would previously have died or been handicapped have been saved by rapid and appropriate medical intervention.

As normal deliveries have become less common, forceps and vacuum deliveries have increased from 4.7 per cent in 1958 to 8.0 per cent in 1970 and up again, substantially according to our

* The surgical cutting of the birth canal to aid delivery.

survey, to 14 per cent in 1981. Caesarian sections have increased from 2.7 per cent in 1958 to 4.5 per cent in 1970 and up again to 10 per cent in 1981.

Many women did experience disappointment when a forceps or Caesarian delivery was deemed necessary, and there were those who expressed doubt as to the need for such intervention. This was especially true of women who felt forceps had become necessary as a result of an induction or an epidural which had not worn off. Few women expressed doubts about their need for a Caesarian. Their relief at having a healthy baby overrode such considerations, and epidurals have increased the pleasure of the experience. It is not surprising, therefore, to find that more than 72 per cent of women enjoyed the delivery of their babies, although there is still much to be done to improve the experience of delivery for those 27 per cent of women who said they did not enjoy it.

Normal deliveries The quotes that follow are typical of many beautiful descriptions of 'normal' birth that we received. The overriding impression is that of pleasure following a birth in which a woman felt it was she who gave birth and secondly enormous gratitude to doctors, midwives and husbands who helped her to give birth 'her way'. **Cheryl** is from Street in Somerset:

The actual birth was a wonderful experience. I was actually doing something by pushing to help our baby to be born. When they told me they could see the top of her head it felt great, and all of a sudden the baby is here and it's nearly all over. Kirsty is absolutely lovely and she was worth every bit of pain and effort.

Virginia, from Colchester, wrote:

An experience I would not have missed for the world! And my husband being with me made it perfect. I could not have managed without him there. Also the doctor who delivered our baby was so *kind, attentive and* so *enthusiastic about it all.*

Ruth, from Belfast:

I was given terrific instructions by my doctor on how to actually push the baby out and I was also allowed to watch the delivery of the head and placenta. It was a truly wonderful experience and my husband also enjoyed it and wouldn't have missed it for all the world.

Margaret, from Hampstead, is a market research consultant. She gave birth at home:

It was wonderful. The baby arrived at dawn and my friend brought my two-year-old in just as the baby was delivered out of my tummy. My body felt so alive and the feeling of the baby's skin and smell of his body were heightened by my delight at being in my own bed with my own family. I had complete confidence in myself and those around me. I knew nothing would go wrong because, for example, if I was allowed to squat the use of forceps was unlikely. Similarly without drugs there would be less foetal and maternal distress.

Alison is from Dudley:

I was a little late getting to the delivery room as I hadn't been too sure about the 'bearing down' feeling I was getting. However, once I'd got down the corridor (with my husband's support), I started pushing the minute I was up on the delivery bed. I felt no pain once I was pushing instead of trying to fight. I only had to pant once and the baby was there. She was put straight on to me and straight on to the breast. That was really beautiful – it was all easier than I'd expected.

Carol is twenty-one and lives in Bow in East London:

I felt secure which I think is most important . . . at the time of birth I was in a lot of pain but when my husband and staff were encouraging me and telling me how the baby's head was in sight I was excited and the feeling of love and relief straight after delivery were beautiful.

Mandy, from Llanidloes in Powys, wrote:

When the head was in sight I was given a chance to see it. The midwife held up a mirror for me to see. What a wonderful experience.

And **Virginia**, from Harrow, said:

The only painkiller I had was at the stage when I wanted to push and was not allowed to – so I had gas and air for about six contractions – . . . I was then able to push effectively, be fully alert and watch the birth. The baby was alert and undrugged which was my main concern.

Brenda, from Harrow Weald, described the thrill of a normal delivery following a previous Caesarian:

I felt they all wanted me to have a natural birth this time. They certainly gave me every encouragement. . . I did not enjoy the pain of bearing down and pushing. Once the baby was born, however, I felt great. A marvellous sense of achievement. I could hardly believe that this time I had done it.

Brenda describes herself after the delivery as 'sore but smug'.

One of the most unusual stories of a normal delivery came from **Janet**, an unmarried student in North Yorkshire. She gave birth at home and unattended. She had had no antenatal care:

I was fortunate because I gave birth standing up and I had a mirror placed on the floor – I could see the baby coming slowly out of the passageway. This is the way I wanted to give birth and it proved successful.

Eleanor is from Helston. She expressed the mixed reaction of many women to delivery. She answered 'yes' and 'no' to the question 'Did you enjoy the birth of your baby?'

Yes, because it was a quick birth and little fuss was made. No, because nobody really enjoys going through that amount of pain even if it is self-inflicted.

Less positive descriptions of normal deliveries came from women with various reservations about the way in which they and their staff handled the birth. This usually involved questions of choice about the position in which a woman was 'allowed' to give birth. Fifty-seven per cent of women said they did not have 'reasonable freedom of choice' in the position in which they gave birth. In other words, more than half the women in our sample may have been unhappy about the position in which they gave birth. Many women felt also they could not have the natural type of birth they had looked forward to. Midwives who were unsympathetic to natural childbirth also met with criticism.

One woman from Surrey told us:

> *I enjoyed the delivery, yes, but my wishes were not met. I wanted to pull the baby out myself, have it lain on my stomach – delay cord-cutting etc. The hospital staff were too uneasy to let this happen i.e. 'midwife distress' rather than 'baby distress'. I was very disappointed about this aspect of delivery. I might as well say that I was told to make my desires known at the birth which I did, but was met with 'Why do you want this or that?' – during labour is hardly the time to enter into a debate about childbirth – the pupils' training was more important than the birth of my baby.*

Mary, from Merseyside, was one of many who commented on lack of choice in the position in which to give birth. This was her fourth baby:

> *Well, it all happened very quickly. The nurses were tremendous, so it was great in comparison to previous labours and births. I do feel that lying on your back is the most awkward way to deliver though; as one's body seems to urge you to sit up. I reckon those medieval 'stools' would be a darn sight more comfortable.*

Margaret, from Leeds, is a teacher. She points to the importance of the sensitivity of medical staff and also the need for explanation, especially when labour is prolonged:

> *One doctor (a man) came into the delivery room and said 'That's what I like to see, my patients writhing in agony.' It was meant as a joke, but it annoyed me intensely.*
>
> *I refused to let them put my feet in stirrups as it was*

uncomfortable and degrading. But they ignored me until I took them out myself.

I wish they had given me a running commentary on what was happening, especially as there was a long time when I didn't seem to be getting anywhere although I was pushing like mad. I felt at a disadvantage when one after another kept having a look but didn't bother to tell me what they saw or encourage more action on my part. It was like limbo.

Vanessa, from Shrewsbury, is a teacher. Delivery, for her, was not the joyful experience she had hoped it would be:

I think I was so unaware of the stage I had reached I just prayed the contractions would stop – my husband tells me I asked the midwife to put me to sleep or kill me during the second stage (I pushed for two hours!). I was relieved and happy when it was all over but did not enjoy it.

Forceps delivery Thirteen per cent of women had their babies delivered by forceps and 1 per cent by vacuum extraction. Women did not enjoy forceps deliveries as much as normal deliveries. More pain was usually felt and a greater amount of postnatal discomfort following stitching and bruising. The baby was also more likely to be bruised. But for most women a regret that the birth had not been normal and natural was the most often expressed response. Other women also regretted some hospitals' policy of preventing their husband's being present at a forceps delivery. **Lesley**, from Stockport, is a shop assistant:

Because of forceps I felt annoyed with myself for not being able to give birth on my own. I had a lot of gas and air and wasn't completely aware of all that was happening which I now regret.

Jennifer, from Pirbright in Surrey, is a veterinary nurse. She was concerned at the effect of a forceps delivery on her baby:

The baby's head did not engage. So the forceps delivery was very difficult. The head was not the right way round therefore the forceps were not put on correctly resulting in bruising and a cut to the face and forehead.

By the time the baby was delivered I felt I had had enough. I could not help the doctors much because I was so drugged with pethidine. I wish I could have enjoyed the birth. I felt so sorry for the baby being born in such a rough way. The doctor described it as a 'tug of war'.

Rona, from Luton, is a teacher. She gave a detailed account of her forceps delivery which was spoiled only by the fact that hospital policy dictated her husband should not be present:

Despite the fact that the labour had been long and a forceps delivery necessary, I enjoyed the birth of my daughter. I was told by a nurse 'with your next contraction the baby will be here' and she was! The only thing that spoilt it was that, due to the fact that it was a forceps delivery, the doctor performing the delivery would not allow my husband to remain in the room. Both my husband and I asked him several times if my husband could stay (he'd been with me all day) but we felt the doctor rather bluntly and unsympathetically refused. A young lady doctor and other staff had already told us it was worth asking, but unlikely that the doctor concerned would allow it. It seems to be hospital policy that husbands aren't allowed to stay for a forceps delivery – rather than each case being taken for its own merits . . . I enjoyed the birth very greatly but could have enjoyed it that little bit more had my husband shared the actual moment . . . Also I hated the fact that the doctor performing the forceps delivery talked about me in the third person ('I haven't seen her have a contraction yet'). Most of the medical staff, however, were very pleasant and encouraging.

Caesarian delivery Ten per cent of women had their children delivered by a Caesarian section. Forty per cent of these were performed under epidural and 60 per cent under general anaesthetic. According to our survey more than twice as many Caesarians were done in 1981 as in 1970.

Paula, from West London, did not feel happy with the way in which a Caesarian was first mentioned:

No previous mention was made of a Caesarian. Up to that point I was expecting an induction. The senior houseman came to my bedside to announce that they would deliver the following day. 'We're going to do it tomorrow,' he said. He then presented me with a form to sign and as I read it I saw the word operation. 'Operation?' I said. 'Oh yes,' he replied, 'didn't they tell you we're going to deliver you by Caesarian?' 'No, you're supposed to be telling me now.'

However, she goes on:

One of the happiest moments of my life was when I woke up to my husband's words, 'We have a son.'

Christine, from Muswell Hill, is unmarried. Her first baby was born mentally handicapped and slightly spastic after a difficult delivery with a displaced pelvic bone:

As I had a Caesarian section everything was explained to me beforehand by the surgeon and the anaesthetist. I was told to ask as many questions as I liked.

I was made to feel as though I was very important and not just another patient. I was asked whether or not I wanted my parents to see the baby before I was awakened.

Mary, from Didcot in Oxfordshire, praised her hospital's handling of an emergency Caesarian:

I had been suffering from high blood pressure so I was told to come in to be induced. Also after an internal examination the baby's hand and arm were found to be over the head so I had an emergency Caesarian section. My preparation for the Caesarian was superb – everything explained and great kindness and sympathy expressed.

Episiotomy – To cut, to tear or to stretch

The increasing popularity of episiotomies* amongst obstetricians is demonstrated by the findings of this survey. According to Sheila Kitzinger (*Episiotomy – Physical and Emotional Aspects*, National Childbirth Trust, 1981) the incidence of episiotomy has

* The cutting of the birth canal to aid the birth.

increased from 22 per cent in 1968 to 37 per cent in 1973. In 1979 it was performed in well over 50 per cent of deliveries and in some hospitals nearly every first-time mother was given an episiotomy. According to our survey half of all women had an episiotomy (a few tore as well as being cut). Twenty-seven per cent of women had no episiotomy and no tear. However, a surprising 22 per cent had a spontaneous tear which had to be stitched. Sheila Kitzinger has argued convincingly that 'episiotomy is an example of an intervention which has been introduced into obstetric practice without accurate assessment and without asking women what they prefer'. What did women in our survey feel about episiotomies and tears?

The strongest comments on episiotomies and tears came firstly from women who had to wait a long time for a doctor to come and put stitches in – sometimes for several hours. When the stitches were put in they were frequently painful and in some cases more painful than the delivery. Secondly, many women mentioned with great gratitude midwives who helped them to give birth in such a way as to avoid the need for an episiotomy or a tear – by slow and gentle stretching. Other women said they wished they had been cut rather than torn.

First some comments from women who had to wait to be stitched up or found it very painful. This seemed frequently to apply to women delivered in GP units by a midwife. The stitching had to be done by a GP who was not always available. **Denise** wrote:

I was left for ages in the delivery room afterwards, two hours waiting to be stitched up by my GP and another two before I was washed and taken back to the ward. It wasn't the nurses' fault. There were only two on duty and they had another woman delivering just after me.

Gillian was delivered in a GP unit:

The birth was straightforward but I tore and had to be stitched. The doctor who stitched me did it completely wrong and the midwife who delivered the baby insisted he did it again. This was extremely painful and to make matters worse the doctor left me with my legs up and completely open to infection. I was in this position for some twenty minutes. In my opinion this was the most painful experience I've ever had.

These women commented on how they would have preferred a 'cut' to a 'tear'. **Margaret**, from Hull:

The delivery went very smoothly until the crowning. I wish I had been cut instead of tearing in quite a few places. The worst part was the stitches. I could feel considerable pain when the stitches were put in outside the area under the anaesthetic . In my opinion I should have had more than one injection.

Eileen is unmarried and is a stablegirl from Helston in Cornwall. She had a difficult first delivery at home. Midwives are not normally expected to do episiotomies. This may lead to a situation where a woman may not be able to have an episiotomy – especially if it is a home delivery or an isolated GP unit delivery:

The birth was much harder work than I imagined and much more painful. I would have appreciated an episiotomy, although when labour began I was dead against it. Being stitched was agony and so was having them out.

Kirsty, from Stafford, felt happy when delivery was speeded up with the aid of a 'cut':

I knew the baby was stuck but they wouldn't listen. It took my blood pressure to sort it out. I was so relieved when a different doctor came and explained what was going to happen. I felt nothing but relief when I was cut and the baby came out alive.

Other women were deeply grateful to midwives and doctors who enabled them to give birth *without* a cut or tear. Where delivery was gradual and there was no reason to get the baby out in a hurry, the happiest women are those who avoid both a tear and a cut. The lack of stitches is especially appreciated in the post-natal period when they can cause a lot of pain – sometimes even for months afterwards. **Jean** is from Merseyside. She was delivered at a consultant unit in Liverpool:

The midwife who delivered my baby was very nice and cheerful and as I had always been stitched with my other children I had dreaded getting them again. She said she would help me and I would not have to have them. I did not; I personally feel this was due to her care.

Katherine, from Sheffield, felt that a slower delivery would have prevented her tearing. She was induced:

> *The drip I had to start the labour made everything happen too fast. Instead of the baby gradually being born so that I could stretch he came out like a rocket which is probably why I tore. My body hadn't a chance to adjust.*

Glynis, from St Austell in Cornwall, has three young children. She sums up the feelings of many women – with good medical support the ideal situation is one in which neither an episiotomy nor a tear occurs. But this requires a very special kind of midwife or doctor who is committed to this ideal:

> *I was impressed because of the way the midwife managed to deliver the baby so quickly, but collectedly and calmly. He was a pound heavier than my heaviest and I've always had episiotomies and several problems, but she was determined not to cut me unless absolutely necessary; even though I'm small. It worked!*

Penny is from Boston in Lincolnshire. She emphasized the fact that time spent helping a woman deliver her baby can avoid the need for a cut or a tear:

> *This time they weren't busy, so I wasn't stranded hopelessly on my back on a monitor. The staff had time to check themselves that everything went OK. I had one bad hour – the rest of the time I felt relaxed and confident – hence I think no episiotomy. The amount of time staff can devote to you makes all the difference.*

It seems that women prefer to be cut than to tear, but best of all, as with roughly a quarter of our survey, they want to be helped to avoid the need for either. But where there is a virtual assumption that an episiotomy will be performed, the skills involved in avoiding the need for a cut or tear may be lost.

Midwives

A midwife is unique in the medical world of doctors and nurses. She is neither a nurse nor a doctor – she is a professional, trained to work with a large amount of independence and responsibility, calling on the obstetrician or GP when the pregnancy or labour looks as though it is getting into difficulty. She is trained to care for women with normal pregnancies and normal deliveries.

The 'medical takeover' of pregnancy and childbirth has had a profound effect on the midwife's role, and especially so in hospital. With the increasing dominance of the obstetrician, the midwife has become, in many ways, no more than a maternity nurse. Her status is reduced and the special and equal relationship which she was previously able to build up with women has been adversely affected. We have already seen how women attending hospital antenatal clinics are less likely to find their midwife 'helpful and understanding' than in the local GP clinics where the community midwife still retains most aspects of her traditional and unique status.

In hospital her job in the antenatal period has become more and more 'task orientated' and less and less 'woman orientated'. Her job is to test urine, take blood pressure etc. rather than to be responsible for a certain group of women whose entire needs, medical or non-medical, are given consideration. Midwives seem to have allowed obstetricians to turn them into nurses whose job is to keep clinics running efficiently rather than to care for women.

It is not just the profession of midwifery which has suffered as a result of this trend (it's now increasingly difficult to attract new recruits), women have suffered too. They have lost a friend and gained an impersonal clinic.

As we go from pregnancy to labour and delivery a rather different picture emerges. Women are much happier with their care at delivery than in the antenatal period. The main reason for this is likely to be that the midwife is allowed to *be* a midwife during labour/delivery in a way that she is not in the clinics.

By and large it is the midwife who makes or breaks a happy delivery. About half of the women in our survey were delivered by midwives without the presence of a doctor. Of course the presence of the husband, the amount of preparation etc., are also of great importance, but time and time again, it is the kindness and expert help of the midwife that women describe in writing about their happy experiences.

Midwifery is the cornerstone of a good 'women-orientated' maternity service. A midwife is more likely to have respect for a woman's desire to give birth in her own way and be less tempted to intervene. Her interest and expertise lie in normal labour and she does her best to keep it that way.

Midwives who were already known to women were particularly appreciated. But sadly 73 per cent of women did not know the midwife who was present at the birth. The great advantage of the domino scheme for women is that they are delivered by the community midwife whom they already know. Where hospitals *have* enabled women to get to know the midwife who is to deliver them this has been greatly appreciated. But hospital schedules and the separation of antenatal clinic staff from labour ward staff almost always preclude this.

Here are some typical comments we received about midwives. **Christine**, from Bristol:

The student and midwife who were present during labour were more like friends rather than just doing their job.

Louise, from Cheshire:

I couldn't praise the midwife who delivered my baby highly enough. She told me everything she was doing and why, and she was very sympathetic.

Christine, from Humberside:

The midwife called me by my first name which made it much more friendly. She was super.

Rossalyn, from Newbridge in Gwent, is a state enrolled nurse:

Childbirth seems to need nurses with specialized training – the midwives – and from what I've been told by my unfortunate female friends half the doctors don't know what is going on with a woman in labour.

Fiona, from Preston, was one of many who particularly appreciated the midwife who stayed right thought to the delivery:

The midwife was very helpful. She stayed on to deliver the baby after she should have gone off duty so I wouldn't have to get to know someone else.

Rosemary, from Fareham, is a teacher:

My midwife was fantastic (she was supervising a pupil who did the delivery). We had the lights dimmed to get a friendly relaxed atmosphere. Everything was geared to the friendly intimate atmosphere as in one's home.

Debra, from Poole, said:

The midwife was smashing. She apologized for giving me an enema as she thinks it's not a very nice thing to have. She answered everything I wanted to know. They let me do what I wanted to do in the delivery.

Susan, from Cheltenham, is a teacher:

The hospital provided tapes to play to encourage relaxation – also the midwife was very attentive and encouraging during later stages when contractions became more unpleasant.

Wendy, from Cheshire, wrote:

I found the nurses and particularly the midwife lovely even though I had not met the midwife before. She insisted on taking me back to the ward herself. We got on extremely well and my husband was treated very well too. He was never made to feel that he was in the way.

Susan, from Camberley, also had her local midwife for the delivery:

I requested and I had my own local midwife to attend the birth and she gave me a lot of encouragement when it was needed.

Other women commented appreciatively on midwives who had helped them to have a natural labour and delivery. **Jillian**, from Wirral, is a telephonist:

I wanted a natural birth using the relaxation techniques taught at the antenatal clinic. I was encouraged and helped during labour by the midwife and felt a tremendous sense of achievement when I succeeded.

Janet is from West Yorkshire. She describes what might be considered 'the perfect birth' and much credit for this goes to the midwife's approach:

I came across one midwife who was all for the traditional bright lights, full shave and 'I don't think much of the NCT' approach – but otherwise everyone was very kind. The pupil who delivered Polly was very sympathetic despite having worked for seventeen hours at a stretch (throughout the night) without having had much sleep before that.

The midwife favours a modified 'Leboyer' delivery therefore the lights were dimmed in the delivery room. I only had to push a few times as my labour progressed so quickly. So I was able to enjoy the event. Polly was placed on my abdomen immediately after her birth and she was not expected to cry. She was put to the breast within minutes of her birth – she spent about half-an-hour contentedly sucking. The whole thing was lovely.

Some women regarded midwives with a mixture of awe and fear – almost as if they were being delivered by their headmistress! **Cynthia**, from Runcorn, for one:

They tend to bully you, but in some cases this is necessary, it's for your own good. Nearer to the actual birth you feel it would be so much easier to give up, but you can't, so they have to urge you on.

Elizabeth is from Bolton. Her expectations did not materialize:

I had so much pain I shouted a bit but they did not tell me off as I thought they would.

Amongst so many cheerful and appreciative reports on midwives, there were some that were less so. Some midwives are not so sensitive, or have rigid 'rules' or just don't have time to sit and listen and explain.

Another problem mentioned by many women was the difficulty of adjusting to new staff – especially from the day to the night staff. It certainly appears that midwives are more likely to be rushed and therefore less sympathetic at night than in daytime. Another comment was made about the difficulty of getting the midwife to believe that labour was advanced and delivery imminent!

Problems also arose when midwives couldn't contact husbands or partners. Women felt at the 'mercy' of midwives.

Jean's comments seem to cover virtually all of the few criticisms that were made by women about midwives:

> *The midwife didn't believe that I wanted to push – still I suppose she wouldn't, seeing as she was on the other side of the room putting her gloves on.*
>
> *I was left alone. I even got to the labour bed on my own. The midwife didn't tell me when to push or pant and I delivered the head on my own. My first birth was a beautiful experience. My second I wouldn't wish on anyone.*
>
> *The midwife only was present, and she had to do everything and therefore was rather offhand and short-tempered. In fact downright rude. Apparently she has a reputation for this.*
>
> *I only had freedom of choice because the midwife acted as though I was a complete burden on her and she was absolutely non-caring for me or the baby.*
>
> *When I asked to hold my son the midwife said, 'When I've cleaned up all this mess you've made.' I wasn't told his weight for two and a half hours.*
>
> *Partly because of staff shortages at night at the hospital I felt very lonely at a time when I felt a closeness to someone is needed. The midwife said it was because of 'financial cutbacks'.*
>
> *She refused to telephone my husband even though when he left she'd promised to. I was very upset and couldn't stop crying. Nobody comforted me. I was left completely alone. After nagging for three hours the midwife did phone. My husband was told the wrong weight and he assumed our child was born at 6 a.m. In actual fact he was born at 3.05 a.m.*

Rosemary, from West Yorkshire, did not take to her nurse (or was she a midwife?):

The nurses were far from gentle and definitely not sympathetic. In fact one was downright rude. After several painful intervals the sister said, 'Don't move I'm going to insert one finger.' Anyway, I flinched, and she said, really nastily, 'I don't know how you got bloody pregnant in the first place.' When trying to clean me up a little she said, 'Where's your brush?' I said, 'In my bag.' She got it, then brushed roughly through my hair and the bristle base came away from the handle. She said, 'Couldn't you get a new one?' So I said, 'This is new.'

The ill-considered remark can be very hurtful or discouraging to a woman in labour. Here are two more examples. **Amanda**, from Withington, is an operations analyst:

Other than the restrictions my experience was not too bad. The midwife called me 'one of those NCT types' when I refused help for pain. She said that it was stupid to be a martyr.

Janet is a teacher from Carnforth in Lancashire:

There appeared to be some anxiety on the part of the midwife over delay in the second stage of labour. At one point she said 'The baby will never be born if you don't push harder.' This did not help to reduce tension and anxiety on our part.

Penelope, from Basingstoke, was a midwife. She made an interesting comment on her own training:

I did not particularly enjoy midwifery training and left four months after I qualified. I have not practised it since. None of my set were very impressed with the way mothers were treated at our training hospital and tried to suggest ways of improvement – few of which were adopted.

Loneliness was a real agony for some women and especially so when husbands were not telephoned or when the night staff was on duty and staff shortages more acute. Six per cent of women said they were left alone most of the time during labour. **Jean** had a particularly sad story:

My husband had to leave to look after my son and after that I had no one until I walked into the labour ward after ringing the bell four times. At no time after my husband left at 11.30 p.m. did anyone come and check on me. I felt very lonely and inadequate. My son was born at 3.05 a.m.

Janice's treatment seems to have been inadequate given the fact that she was known to be delivering twins at thirty-six weeks and suggests a lack of appropriate care on this occasion (at night):

I was very frightened and in pain. I was left alone with my husband. Nobody explained anything to me . . . the night duty sister was not sympathetic at all. She kept saying she had other deliveries to attend to – when I complained about my pain and being left alone and I was very frightened. The day staff were marvellous.

Many women commented on the contrast in care they received between day and night staff. Yet nearly 50 per cent of babies in our survey were born during the night. **Jane** is a teacher who had a hard time at night:

The Sister on night duty was impatient and unhelpful. The student nurse on night duty had a heavy cold and did not wear a mask. In the admissions room the Sister hardly spoke to me. Examinations were rough. She was short-tempered when I asked her to be careful as I was beginning a contraction. Morning staff were superb – interested, friendly, supportive and helpful.

It is clear from all these comments that a good midwife is perhaps the single most important factor in determining whether a birth is enjoyed or not. Health authorities could do much to improve the care of pregnant women and women in labour by ensuring that enough midwives are employed. The shortage of midwives which is acute in some areas, and especially seems to affect night duty, is a tragedy. Obstetricians also have a responsibility to see that midwives are allowed to function as midwives and not nurses, and thirdly midwives must see that they do not allow their role to be eroded any further. A good midwife can do so much to create happy new mothers and babies. Let's hope that the trend towards the downgrading of midwifery can be reversed.

Doctors

The doctor was directly involved in the care of 42 per cent of women during labour and 27 per cent of women during delivery. A further 18 per cent were attended 'some of the time' by a doctor during delivery. There is no doubt that the participation of doctors in labour and delivery has greatly increased and is increasing.

Women were more likely to have met the doctor who delivered them beforehand than the midwife. Fifty-two per cent of women had met the doctor before whereas only 27 per cent had met the midwife. This is a reflection of the smaller number of doctors compared with midwives and the fact that doctors work in both antenatal clinic and labour wards. Also women who are attended by their GP will virtually all have met him or her before.

Women seem to be happy with either a male or a female doctor – only 8 per cent said they preferred a male doctor and 11 per cent a female doctor. But most women agreed that it didn't matter what sex a doctor was as long as he or she was understanding. Women do find it harder to relate to the hospital doctor than their GP especially in the antenatal period. As we saw in the previous chapter, only 43 per cent of women found their hospital doctor 'helpful and sympathetic' compared with 69 per cent with the GP. The hospital doctor is usually rushed and therefore concentrates on the purely physical and medical facts and can find it difficult to have a wider perspective.

Women commented less on their doctors than on their midwife. The doctor tended to be a fleeting figure with whom it was difficult to establish a relationship. They were grateful for sympathetic and gentle doctors and upset when doctors were rough in examinations or harsh in tone. They disliked it when doctors spoke about them to students. Other women were deeply grateful for prompt action which saved the lives of their babies.

Kim, from Northumberland, is an SRN:

I think that Dr Godfrey who is the senior registrar at IMM hospital was the most dedicated and sympathetic doctor I have ever met. He delivered my baby and he made me feel extremely relaxed and special. He was fantastic, as all the staff were.

Elizabeth, from Bristol, told us:

The midwife, student midwife and doctor were all young and made me and my husband feel completely at ease. He was not sent out of the room, even during internal examinations. The doctor brought me a cheese roll to eat after I delivered because I hadn't eaten much all day.

Judith was particularly appreciative of her GP although the hospital failed to get hold of him for the delivery. She lives in Northamptonshire:

My doctor requested to be present, but because he was off duty, the hospital refused to call him. He was annoyed with the hospital.

I couldn't have bettered the attention given to me throughout my pregnancy by my GP. After the birth he called in every day throughout my five days' stay in hospital. He does this for all his patients (not just me). He is a very caring and thorough doctor. I cannot express my gratitude to him enough.

Patricia, from Gillingham, disliked her doctor's attitude:

The midwife who was with me in the morning was most helpful. The doctor who sedated me treated me like an idiot who had got herself into a stupid situation.

Husbands and partners

'Father was present at the birth – mother was not!' said **Patricia**, from Gillingham.

Husbands or partners were present during part or all of 92 per cent of labours. Six per cent of women had a friend or relative with them. About 5 per cent of women had no husband, friend or relative with them during labour. Those who suffered most from loneliness were women who, whether because of childcare problems, because the birth happened before the husband could be contacted, or because they had no husband or friend, spent their labour without the comfort and support of a familiar and trusted friend.

Fewer women had a friend or relative or husband with them during delivery than labour. Sixty-one per cent of women had their husband, a friend or relative with them for the birth. Many of those women who did not said it was their own wish (47 per cent). Fourteen per cent of them had no one present on medical grounds. Women having Caesarians under general anaesthetic and those having forceps deliveries were likely not to have a friend, relative or husband with them.

It is hard to believe, reading women's comments about their husbands, that a few years ago it was relatively rare for a husband to be present with his wife during labour and delivery. Perhaps the most significant recent change in the management of labour and delivery from the woman's point of view has been the introduction of the husband into the labour and delivery suite – the recognition that birth is the culmination of nine months thinking, waiting and planning by *both* parents and that to allow the father to share in this supreme moment not only brings the couple closer but gives the father more immediate bonding with his child. Just as new mothers find it harder to bond with a baby they do not have immediate contact with, so the father needs to see, to hold and to love his child from the very beginning.

Another comment made by many women is that their husbands were more supportive after the birth than they might have been had they not been present at it. An appreciation of the tremendous physical feat of giving birth is much greater, and there is more understanding as to why the woman feels so tired in the weeks that follow birth. The hospitals and medical staff that welcomed in husbands and partners, regarding them as central characters rather than as supernumeraries to be tolerated, were greatly appreciated – especially when they ended up having to revive an unconscious husband!

After twenty-eight hours of labour **Alicia**, from Enfield, found her husband more shattered than she was!

> *After twenty-eight hours it was a great relief to get something out of it and it has not put me off at all. It was also amusing*

to find my husband had collapsed at my side and had to be carried out by the doctor, and came back to see me twenty-five minutes later!

If only all hospitals were as 'geared' to the presence of husbands as some clearly are. **Julie's** *husband* described how he was welcomed by the hospital. They live in Wirral:

Although my wife remembers little of her time in labour I found the midwives very helpful, sympathetic and considerate to us both. (I was kept supplied with tea and even ordered a meal.) Anything I asked was fully explained to me – e.g. the workings of all the drugs, the print-out of the scalp monitor and contraction graph. I was also encouraged to help my wife. This was especially so during the final stages. I thought the midwives were very good. Our baby was born soon after the change of staff from evening to night shift and there did not seem to be as many staff on duty. There were several girls in the final stage of labour. The midwives had to rush from one bed to another as births became imminent. Although they were very busy they allowed me to take a photo of the baby in a cot about two minutes after she was born. After seeing the way they worked I have nothing but praise for the staff.

Alva, from Milton Keynes, mentioned, as did many women, the importance of having a husband present to help her give birth in her way:

I felt that if I hadn't had my husband with me they might have tried to push me into having a stronger painkiller which I didn't want.

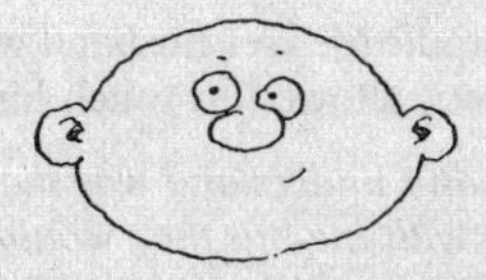

The main difficulty that arose for women was actually achieving their husband's presence in the labour suite at the right time. For various reasons, some of which are apparent in the following quotes, husbands were not always present when their wives deeply wished for their company and support. Hospitals sometimes seemed unwilling to contact husbands and in other cases husbands had transport and childcare problems. Other women found that husbands were not allowed in for forceps or breech deliveries. **Ann** is a physiotherapist from Middlesbrough:

The staff said they would phone my husband when I was nearly due as he had to go home to be with my little girl until my parents arrived. The hospital did not ring until it was too late for him to get there.

Christine, from Lancashire, is a teacher:

My husband rang when I was put on the drip and asked about coming in to be with me. The staff said I would be quite some time yet and to ring again at lunchtime. However, my husband insisted on coming – the baby was born two-and-a-half hours later. If he had taken their advice, I would have laboured completely without his assistance and comfort.

I was not told I was to have forceps. I was pushing normally then my husband was sent out and I was put on stirrups etc. without anything being said to me to reassure me – it was rather a frightening and distressing experience. I feel it would have been reassuring to have my husband present. He understood what a forceps delivery entailed.

Linda, from Bradford, wrote:

On the labour ward they were very good apart from when I wanted my husband to be with me during the birth and they wouldn't let him because the baby was breech, which I strongly disagree with.

This came as a great upset to us both.

Fiona is also from Bradford. Her husband was allowed in at the birth, but then was not allowed to touch his baby!

. . . one thing I didn't understand was that they encouraged my husband to be with me but they wouldn't let him touch the baby. Surely they could have given him a sterile gown or something if they were worried about infection . . . as it was my husband didn't feel the baby was his until we got him home.

Listening and explaining

In answer to the question 'Were you told what was happening during delivery?' 11 per cent of women in the survey answered 'hardly at all' and 16 per cent 'some of the time'. One of the most striking findings of this survey was the difficulty some women had in finding out what was happening to them. Ignorance can lead to fear which can lead to tension and a less relaxed labour and delivery. Those women who were unsure about what was happening or what stage they had reached were more likely to panic or lose control.

Even more important was the difficulty women had in getting the medical staff to listen and take notice of what they were saying.

> *I told them the baby was on the way, but they wouldn't believe me.*

> *. . . they told me I had hours to go – I delivered ten minutes later.*

These kinds of comments occurred often. Are midwives and doctors sometimes so rushed that they just hope the birth is not imminent, or is the woman herself sometimes a more reliable guide to imminent birth than, for example, examining the size of the cervix?

Whatever the reason, many women complained that nobody believed them when they were certain that they were pushing the baby out. Midwives were sometimes to be found putting their gloves on when the baby was emerging. Other women experienced the great discomfort of being moved from labour ward to delivery suite with the delivery occurring virtually in the corridor. A few women never made it to the delivery suite and gave birth in the more relaxed surroundings of the labour room. Those hospitals which did not move women for the delivery did not have this problem. **Violet**, from Liverpool, is thirty-six, and she found herself in an ideal situation:

> *Every question I asked was answered. The machines which were new to me were explained. I knew exactly what was going on.*

The need for explanation when things go wrong is particularly great. **Kim**, from Watford, said:

During labour any questions I asked were answered completely to my satisfaction. When things went wrong afterwards with the afterbirth the doctor explained to me and my husband exactly what was going on before and after the operation.

Women who had lost a previous baby were especially vulnerable to lack of explanation. **Pamela** is a schoolteacher from Tunbridge Wells. Her second baby was born with spina bifida and died fifteen minutes after delivery:

The staff were aware of the death of my second baby and were extremely sympathetic to my anxious state during delivery.

The importance to women of *how* they are spoken to as well as *what* was said to them was evident from many reports. Explanation and 'instructions' can be wasted if the woman does not feel that the staff are in partnership with her and are not just there to issue orders. **Susan**, from Blackpool, put it this way:

Sometimes I felt very distant as if to them it's just another job, which I suppose it is, but I think you should be made to feel individual.

Gillian, from Lincoln, made a comment which was typical of many:

They didn't talk to *me but* at *me. They did remind me when to push but when they found the cord round the neck they only talked together and not to me.*

Janice, from Gravesend, is a secretary:

I wasn't told what was happening and kept being shouted at to push. I was frightened and thought I wasn't doing it right and that it was my fault and I didn't realize that it couldn't be born because of the size of the head in relation to the pelvis. Because of obvious pain I said the painkillers weren't working. I was just told to take gas and air. I had things like my waters broken and I wasn't told what was happening.

Fear causes tension which can make pain more difficult to control. Many women commented on how the sympathy and 'running commentary' of the midwife helped them to avoid the use of any drugs. Conversely, perhaps the administration of painkillers is sometimes a substitute for sympathy.

A large number of comments came from women about the difficulty of getting midwives and doctors to believe that the birth was imminent. Here is a selection. **Janet**, from Leeds, wrote:

> *The only criticism I have is that medical people tend to give you no credit for knowing what is going on – e.g. when you tell them the baby is coming, they reply that it can't be, it is not ready. And out it pops.*

Angela is from Hove:

> *I was a bit disconcerted when I felt the urge to push and the midwife told me not to as nothing would happen for ages. My daughter was born twenty-five minutes later.*

Kim, from Alford in Lancashire, found it difficult to convince the sister (midwives) that her baby was imminent. She also described the discomfort of having her waters broken – especially when she did not know they were going to do it:

> *With my first baby my waters did not go until the baby was almost arriving. This time they did it and it was very painful. My pains then slowed down. I do not think they should have done it, also they did not tell me. She just said she was going to have a feel. I was in a lot of pain and when the doctor came she said my baby would not come for about four to five hours. This was about 8.15 p.m. When they had all gone I told the pupil midwife to get someone as I wanted to push. The nurse would not go at first, and I had to push her. The doctor came back and told me that the baby was not ready to come for another few hours – my baby was born ten to*

fifteen minutes later. It made me mad – as if they were having the baby not me. How do they know how I feel?

The effect that miscalculating the progress of labour can have on the use of painkillers is described by **Ann**, from Worcester:

I was told that I had hours to go – up till then I had refused pethidine – but with that I was defeated so I agreed to the injection. I kept telling everyone I could feel the head, they kept saying 'you're not ready yet'. When they did eventually believe me I was rushed to the delivery room and my daughter was born in a hurry without anyone being scrubbed up or with gowns and masks.

Jennifer, from Kettering, pointed to the way that routine hourly checks by midwives can mean that imminent delivery can be missed. Her story also shows how internal examinations do not always seem to give a reliable indication of how near a woman is to delivery:

I kept asking the midwife how long it would be before the baby would be delivered and they kept saying 'not long'. The pains were coming one after the other at four o'clock. I kept telling the nurse and she said I would have to wait until five o'clock before she could do an internal examination. In the end the midwife examined me at 4.15 and said I was only half-way there but the pains were very bad by now and the baby was born at 5.08. When I was making moaning noises because of the pain I was just told to shut up.

This section has shown that in some cases the judgement as to when a baby will be born can be a very inexact 'science'. Perhaps if women were listened to, fewer 'panic' deliveries would have to be done – and such deliveries are less likely to be relaxed than those that have been anticipated and prepared for.

Life and death

Twenty-one per cent of babies in our survey had what their mothers considered to be serious problems during labour or delivery. Five per cent of women reported that their babies were not born healthy. This includes those babies that died of congenital abnormalities, prematurity, or were stillborn. It also includes a larger number of babies who were born with congenital defects such as spina bifida, cleft palates and dislocation of the hips, and also babies who needed special or intensive care in the first days or weeks to help their breathing etc. Some babies developed jaundice and a few had heart defects. The figure of 5 per cent compares with a generally accepted figure that around 5 per cent of all babies are born with some degree of handicap or die at or around the time of birth.

Very few women who lost their babies felt that the death could have been avoided. Most women felt that either the death was unavoidable because of a congenital defect (although some wished that this had been detected in pregnancy) while others felt that the doctors and nurses had done everything possible to save the life of their sick or very small baby.

Five per cent of babies weighed less than 2,500 grams (5lb 8oz) the weight below which physical problems are far more likely to arise. (This compares with the 7.3 per cent national figure). Two per cent of all babies weighed less than 2,000 grams (4lb 7oz) and 1 per cent less than 1,500 grams (3lb 5oz). It is these very tiny babies who usually spend weeks being cared for with great devotion and skill in intensive care units. These units have developed in the last ten years and have done much to reduce the high death rates previously associated with very tiny babies.

It is of some concern that some very small babies did not get transferred to expert units but remained in local special care baby units where they did not always thrive. There is a nationwide shortage of intensive care cots and sometimes an unwillingness on the part of a few paediatricians to transfer very sick or tiny babies who might benefit from a more sophisticated type of care than they can offer.

Intensive care is all the more important today because of the increased tendency for obstetricians to deliver tiny babies by 'elective' Caesarian. This is done in order to save the life of a baby which is not growing and is at risk, therefore, of dying before the end of the pregnancy. These small and sometimes fragile babies are especially in need of expert care after the birth. Twelve per cent of babies in our survey spent some time in a special care baby unit. Thirty-nine per cent spent less than twenty-four hours in a unit while 22 per cent spent more than seven days (13 per cent spent more than fourteen days).

Those women who felt the death or handicap of their child could have been avoided described what they felt to be inadequate medical care of them and their child. Fourteen per cent of women said they developed serious problems during labour or delivery which if not promply dealt with could have put the baby severely at risk – a haemorrhage for example. The agony and misery felt by women who lost their babies was made even more unbearable when there was a conviction that it could have been avoided.

Less than half a per cent of women in our survey had twins. Twins were usually – but not always – diagnosed before birth. Twins were particularly at risk during and after delivery if they were delivered in a small, less well-equipped hospital. It is normal for a paediatrician to be present at the delivery of twins as they are more often born underweight or unhealthy than single babies.

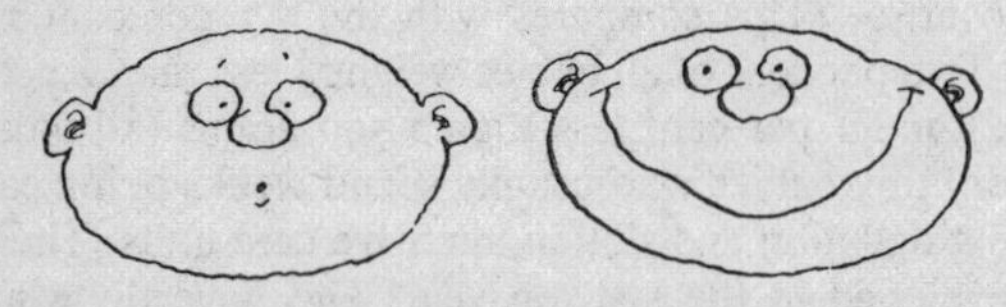

It is clear from the various stories we record about emergencies that many babies might not be alive and healthy today if it had not been for prompt and appropriate intervention at the right time. However, emergency action is always second best to an anticipated difficulty. It is obviously preferable for both the mother and baby if a difficulty is predicted. If there is to be a breech birth, twins or a premature birth, or the mother has high blood pressure or a very small pelvis, appropriate plans ought to be made in advance as opposed to a rushed response to an emergency. Obviously there will always be emergencies which cannot be predicted – a sudden premature delivery or the cord round the baby's neck, but the aim of good antenatal care is to reduce these to a minimum and to ensure that any woman likely to develop difficulties is delivered in the best-equipped hospital.

The quotes that follow cover a wide range of responses to difficult deliveries – both emergency and anticipated. The overwhelming feeling expressed by women who have been through this experience is intense gratitude to those expert and dedicated staff who have saved both the lives and the health of their babies.

In all the deliveries that are described in these quotes, prompt action was taken to deliver babies who might otherwise have suffered severe consequences. It is salutory to contemplate that it is situations such as these which, before the development of modern obstetrics, might have resulted in either the death or handicap of the baby, or the death of the mother. **Diane**, from Orpington, is a secretary:

I went to the delivery room and gave birth to a foot but the doctor then realized that the baby would not be able to come out that way.

The specialist was around at the time so, as I was a breech, it was decided to deliver it in front of several students.

Firstly he was breech, and secondly his foot was already outside when a Caesarian was decided on and we had to be rushed like that to the Caesar theatre.

I felt the right action was taken at the right time.

Mary is from Shropshire:

I was taken in as an emergency with placenta abruption. The care I received during the subsequent three nights when I went in and out of false labour was excellent. I was allowed to be driven in by my husband with the midwife who came to the house after I had started bleeding.*

Essel, a short story writer from Oxford, was one of various women who wrote in praise of the John Radcliffe Hospital in Oxford and their handling of a difficult situation:

I went into hospital early because of high blood pressure and a large baby being very low down.

It was a most painful experience though hospital staff were absolutely marvellous the whole time which made things a little easier.

The baby was distressed and I had high blood pressure. Labour was going too slowly.

A blood sample from the baby's head showed signs of distress. The baby needed to come out fast.

* When the placenta parts from the womb.

I was told step by step what was happening and why, and was asked continually if I wanted to know anything.

I did not know much about it after going into the theatre.

Sandra, from Winchester, was lucky to be in hospital when bleeding started:

I was admitted to hospital after an antenatal check-up because the baby was not moving as much as it should do. So they wanted to do some movement tests on the monitor which would take a least two days. Whilst I was in for tests I started losing blood which was the afterbirth coming away and therefore I had to have an emergency Caesarian. When I was admitted I was told that the baby's head was engaged but obviously it was not – it was the afterbirth. If I had not been in hospital then I would have lost the baby.

Jacqui, from Twickenham, liked the way Queen Charlotte's Hospital, London, handled her emergency:

The baby was showing signs of stress and the head was in the wrong position. It was a very good operation. My partner stayed throughout and we could listen to pop music (new idea). Very good and relaxing.

Nadia, from Nottinghamshire, is forty-two. She probably owes her life to an emergency Caesarian:

I became very ill with high blood pressure and my kidneys began to fail so I was rushed down to theatre on the seventh of May.

As it was under general anaesthetic I wasn't awake until about an hour or two later and I had to be given special care all night. I was under constant supervision.

Women who lost their babies reacted in various ways, depending to some extent on the reasons for the baby's death.

Heather felt rightly or wrongly that a misreading of the monitor led to the death of her baby. One doctor told her if a Caesarian had been performed when the first signs of distress were seen – at least by her – then the baby might have been saved.

I had a false labour of two hours two weeks before the actual birth. The cord must have held the baby back because afterwards she was so low I felt I was sitting on her. The four hours of induced labour I enjoyed because my baby was on its way, but when I watched her die on the monitor and felt her last kick, the next fifteen hours of intense labour was horrific knowing she was dead.

After about four hours of labour I noticed the monitor reading dropping, I knew our baby was in trouble, so I rang the bell; it was ages before two auxiliary nurses came. They tapped the machine saying it was wrong. I insisted it wasn't and the baby needed help. After five minutes they called the sister who pulled at the electrode on the baby's head and tapped the machine. I told her I was being induced because of the baby's heart – please do something – she eventually brought three doctors. They did the same and also used the sonic aid – too late – my baby kicked me once and died.

In conclusion, when she was born they found the cord had strangled her. It was wrapped round her neck eight times. Afterwards the doctor told my husband that there was almost 5 feet of umbilical cord and they hadn't seen it before in any other pregnancy. One consultant told us they had chosen the wrong cause for slowing the heart rate out of the possible reasons and that if a Caesarian had been performed our baby probably would have lived.

She describes her husband's and her own feelings in this way:

The grief was indescribable and unbearable – the worst hours of both my husband's and my lives.

Sally Ann's baby died because of a congenital abnormality. She is a laboratory technician from Hertfordshire:

An ultrasound scan was done after admission to hospital. Following that, the membranes were broken to speed labour as the doctor had doubts as to the baby's normality, but my husband and I were unaware that anything was possibly wrong.

The baby was born with anencephaly and only expected to live a few hours. He survived thirty-nine hours.

The doctor and midwives were very sympathetic especially when the baby's abnormality was detected. The baby was removed immediately so that I should not see him until he was completely covered.

I didn't have any reason to suspect anything was wrong with the baby so yes, I did enjoy the birth. I requested that I shouldn't hold the baby and I only saw and touched him once by request about three hours after the birth when he was christened.

Double trouble?

One set of twins is born in every eighty births according to official figures. Our survey had twenty-two sets of twins which is a ratio of one in two hundred and seventy.

Twins are specially at risk of death because they tend to be premature and also smaller than single babies. Their birth can also be more hazardous.

Jennifer, from Pudsey, had twins at twenty-three weeks weighing 450 and 540 grams each, and both died:

It was very upsetting to go through a natural birth knowing that your babies would be stillborn or only live for a few minutes. [A scan showed twins at twenty weeks.] The babies were both seriously underweight [and died soon after birth] . . . I was told at every stage what and why things were happening. I couldn't have had better attention – the staff were marvellous.

She describes her feelings a few days later. She felt:

very cruelly treated – why me? By the fifth day I felt much better – I was coming to terms with it – I would rather it be this way than have brain-damaged babies – which was a possibility apparently. I'm now looking forward to trying again!

Sheila, from Farnborough in Hampshire, had not been diagnosed as having twins until five hours before they were born. She had exclusive GP antenatal care and no scan. The delivery was complicated but fortunately she had been transferred to a consultant unit:

The twins I was having were being monitored and one was showing foetal distress on the heartbeat. The first one couldn't get further down as the other baby was in the way

. . . they were very tactful and understanding while confirming that it was twins and kept me informed.

She had an emergency Caesarian and delivered two boys – one 5lb 3oz and the other 6lb 8oz. Her story shows up clearly the importance of knowing that twins are on the way and that therefore delivery occurs in a consultant unit with good paediatric care. **Stella**, from Northumberland, wrote:

Originally I intended to have a home confinement with my community midwife but after twins had been confirmed with the ultrasound scan, I decided to go to hospital. I finally went to hospital with high blood pressure at thirty-eight weeks pregnant and was induced for the safety of the babies. My community midwife delivered my two babies safely. My consultant and several other doctors were present at the births (Ashington Maternity Unit, Northumberland) . . . the second twin was lying in a breech position but she did turn when my first baby was born normally and had the cord around her neck. Oxytocin was used to make my womb contract so as to get her born quickly . . . I felt very pleased and relieved when it was all over. I was pleased I refused pethidine this time as I was more aware and the two babies were better for it. I wore my own nightie for the delivery which made me feel better and I refused to be strapped down by a monitor as it would have made labour more painful. I was more relaxed because my midwife was with me.

Her son weighed 6lb 7oz and her daughter 7lb 2oz.

But the arrival of twins can be a very mixed blessing . . . **Denise** had had an ultrasound scan but it failed to pick up the fact that she was expecting twins. She already had one pair of twins and worked as a hospital domestic until thirty-six weeks when the hospital realized it was twins again. She produced two six-pound boys two weeks after stopping work. She plans to return to work for 'financial reasons' when the babies are six months old. She describes her pregnancy as enjoyable:

. . . up to about thirty-six weeks when I found it was twins again I found myself very upset and anxious about how I was going to cope financially.

She describes her feelings after the birth as '*very unhappy . . .*

crying most of the time up to two weeks after the birth . . unable to cope . . .'

We had one set of triplets in the survey. Amy, Eve and Lucy weighing 4lb, 4lb 6oz, and 5lb were all hale and hearty and born to **Hazel** from Norwich. The tremendous importance of good antenatal and delivery care where a multiple birth is expected was well explained by Hazel:

> *. . . once a multiple birth was expected they [the hospital staff] could not have been more helpful. At twenty-eight weeks I became an in-patient although I was allowed home for weekends. The babies' heartbeats were checked daily, weekly blood tests were done, and a fortnightly injection was given to develop the babies' lungs in case they were premature. I was seen daily by a doctor, and nursing staff were always available. The doctors and nurses were both very friendly and helpful spending lots of time explaining things as I asked about them . . .*

At thirty-five weeks Hazel was given:

> *an epidural Caesarian as I was having triplets and because I have a bicornate uterus (double womb) with one baby in one side and two in the other.*

Getting to know you

Cuddling and putting the baby to the breast immediately after he or she is born can be an immensely important and pleasurable experience for the new mother (and father). The longer the gap between birth and cuddling the more difficult it can be for the mother and father to develop that loving, tender, and almost possessive feeling which is so vital to the healthy and happy future of the baby.

Reasons why babies are not given directly to their mothers after birth fall into roughly two areas. Firstly, a very sick or tiny baby will need immediate medical attention – whether it needs resuscitation to get its breathing going or an incubator to warm it up. However, there still seem to be examples of babies being kept from their mothers for reasons such as weighing and bathing. A few midwives still hold to a now old-fashioned view that newborn babies must be bathed before they are fit to be held by their own mothers.

Twenty-four per cent of *That's Life* mothers did not have their babies given to them immediately after birth. Nineteen per cent of all mothers were given their baby within one hour and 5 per cent within days. Those babies who were not healthy at birth (5 per cent) were usually in need of some medical attention or a stay in a special care unit.

In addition there were babies who were basically healthy but needed observation or a little treatment in the special care unit. Twelve per cent of all babies spent some time in such a unit, but nearly 40 per cent of these babies were only in a unit for twenty-four hours or less, so were probably not seriously ill.

The survey and comments certainly suggest that some babies who could have been given the comfort of immediate contact with their mother did not get it. Twenty per cent of women said they did not feel they had reasonable freedom of choice about when the baby was given to them after delivery.

There can be no doubt that it is of the utmost significance to a mother to hold her baby as soon as it is delivered – preferably to have the baby placed first on the tummy and then into her arms. The descriptions we received from women who were able to do this were moving and speak louder than any statistics. It is hard and sad to realize that there are hospitals where handing the baby to its mother immediately after birth, assuming it does not need medical help, is not automatic. It is also worth noting again the great contribution that epidurals have made and are increasingly making to those women who have a Caesarian. For them it is now possible to hold their baby as soon as he or she is lifted out of the womb.

These are some typical comments on how it felt to hold the baby immediately after birth. **Janet**, from Exeter, wrote:

> *Fantastic, as it only took me a short time in labour. But the best thing was I was given the baby to hold whilst the sister cut the cord and it was an indescribable event.*

Lesley, from Sheffield, is a teacher. This was her third baby after losing two babies with neural tube defects:

She was put on my stomach straight away. She cried very quickly. As she was a breech delivery there was no moulding of the head. The relief and emotion I felt when the paediatrician told me that she was normal was indescribable.

Violet is from Merseyside:

When the baby was born he was put on my chest immediately. I just wanted to cuddle him. Then he was wrapped up and put in a cot while I was stitched. I was given him back afterwards and we went to the ward together.

Even women who deliver sick or tiny babies can be helped to bond with them. **Helen**, from Devon, described a hospital's approach to mothers of sick babies which reveals a real understanding of the importance of closeness between mother and baby from the outset – even if only through a photograph:

I was told he was upstairs. The sister was very nice when she told me, and when I had come out of the anaesthetic I was given a Polaroid photograph of him in his incubator as I could not get up to see him. This is a wonderful thing that they give all mothers who cannot see the baby straight away.

Some women were less fortunate. **Angela**, from Croydon, had her baby at home but found that her own midwife was off duty when she delivered and she had a replacement midwife:

I was allowed to hold him but I wanted to feed him straight away, but the midwife said 'my mothers' babies wait till they're washed' and proceeded to take one-and-half to two hours to clean up and give him back to me.

Karen, from Bromley, is a secretary:

After his birth I kept asking to be allowed to feed him, but all the staff were too busy doing other things to hand him to me. After about two hours of being stitched up etc. I was finally given my baby. The nurse was pushy and jerked baby's head about to force him to take the nipple into his mouth. She seemed to be in a hurry to get on with other things and I felt very rushed and uncomfortable. Then, when he was finally feeding she stopped him saying he had had enough.

Another **Karen** was not treated well after the birth:

I wanted to breastfeed her straight away as I did with my first baby. I asked the midwife who said I could after I had been cleaned up. She then went away and I didn't see her again. I asked a nurse who came in with the doctor to do my stitches and she said the same and disappeared. I asked a cleaning lady to ask someone for me and another nurse came and said they were very busy but she would try to get someone to clean me then I could feed her.

I waited for about another fifteen minutes and no one came. It was now about one hour after the birth and I could see my baby but I could not reach her. She had been sucking a towel so I knew she would breastfeed but by this time she was becoming drowsy. In one last attempt I pressed the emergency buzzer because I was determined to feed her and after this someone was sent to clean me and give me the baby to feed.

Apart from this, the doctor who did my stitches was very unsympathetic and hardly said a word to me. He was talking to the nurse all the time about how he was overworked, and no one made me a cup of tea after the birth!

Katherine is from Hayling Island. She is a teacher and, like many first-time mothers, felt bewildered:

The baby was wrapped and his eyes cleaned before being given to me. I expected him to be put naked on my chest. They forgot to put him to the breast and I was too bewildered to ask. I think this contributed to his rejection of the breast later. If I had another child I would make sure this was done as I wanted.

Pamela is from Warwickshire. She is an hotel accountant. Like Katherine she was a first-time mother and felt too afraid to ask for what she wanted. She describes clearly the effect this had on her feelings for her daughter:

I felt very deprived of the actual moment of birth [a Caesarian with general anaesthetic] which was not helped by the time lapse between the birth and me holding my daughter.

I felt a stranger for some time – as though it was someone else's baby I was admiring. It took me a day, at least, before I felt totally maternal towards my baby and have never looked back since that moment. I felt the hospital let me down as, not knowing the routine, I was afraid to 'demand' to see and hold my daughter, so just left it to them.

Paula, from Luton, had a normal delivery (her second baby) but found difficulty in keeping her baby with her once back in the ward:

Until I got home I didn't feel it was my baby – just something I fed when they brought her to me. Four hours after the birth in the ward I asked to see my baby to really look at her – the nurse brought her and stood there waiting to take her back – I just wanted some privacy to say hello to her.

Immediate cuddling of the baby by the mother after birth (and beyond) is immensely important for both mother and baby. Unless there are vital medical reasons to prevent it hopefully all mothers in the future will be given their babies immediately after birth. With 20 per cent of women saying they were not given a choice on this there is still great scope for a better and more natural approach to those vital and valuable minutes after the baby is born.

Second time around

So many women commented on how much happier their second, third or fourth deliveries were than their first that this section is devoted entirely to these contrasts. Do women find delivery easier the more experienced they are or are hospitals gradually becoming more aware of the importance of letting women give birth as naturally as possible, with as much choice and as little intervention as possible? The quotes that follow certainly give a firm impression of change in the last few years and change in the right direction (especially in the less routine use of pethidine and gas and air). Sixty-two per cent of women had already had at least one baby, 68 per cent of these were having their second child, 23 per cent, their third, 5 per cent their fourth and 1 per cent their fifth. **Lynn**, from Bexley Heath, wrote:

My previous experience of childbirth was horrific, ending in a forceps delivery without anaesthetic. It took me five-and-a-half years to pluck up courage to try again but this time it was straightforward and the attitude of the medical staff more sympathetic – despite the fact that I was less in need of sympathy.

Jennifer is from Cheltenham:

Although I sometimes had to ask for advice, e.g. when to push, and what was happening, I felt I was in control of the situation and not being told *what to do. I made the decision to sit up and see my baby being born and to put him to the breast immediately after delivery and no one tried to influence these decisions.*

It had everything I had missed when my first baby was born. I felt like a normal person performing a basic human function. I was not just an object of medical observation.

Susan, from Chepstow in Gwent, wrote:

With my first baby I found that when he was born I was sleepy and half-soaked with drugs and it didn't register when he was born. With this baby I was wide awake and fully aware of what was happening and more in control of the situation.

Carole, from Derby, was pleasantly surprised:

Although I didn't want to go to Derby City Hospital, as I'd had a rough time there with my first child, I found the attitude seemed to have changed and everyone was helpful.

June, from Merthyr Tydfil, had her baby at Aberdare General Hospital:

It was so unlike the first labour that it was a totally new experience – the type you read about when you feel everything is in control what with breathing correctly etc.

As I was so drugged with pethidine in my first labour I asked not to be given it this time so the midwife explained about the using of gas and oxygen. I could feel the desire to laugh (I didn't last time) and felt totally in control and wide awake.

Madeleine is from Poole:

My first birth I'd had pethidine. I was drowsy so I couldn't push. My husband was sent out and forceps used. I didn't want to hold my first child as I felt too drugged, unsafe, frightened I'd drop him. This time it was wonderful I was in control of the situation, no drugs to spoil it. I held my son and was able to enjoy every minute of the birth.

Carolyn, from Cheltenham, wrote:

Having suffered a very difficult and traumatic labour and delivery with my first child, I found this one wonderful. The second she was born I woke up properly, forgot the pain and felt enormously happy, fulfilled and satisfied.

The outlook is encouraging for women giving birth in Britain. If these stories are a sign of a general trend towards a more humanitarian, personal and natural approach to birth in our hospitals women, their husbands and their babies will feel more and more happy with their care.

Giving birth is an intensely important event. The future happiness of the new mother, father and baby is greatly enhanced by a relaxed labour and delivery, and immediate physical contact after birth. It is clear from this chapter that choice in *how* and *where* birth occurs is vital.

4 Who Cares for the Carer? – Results and Reactions

Once the baby is born all kinds of challenges and problems present themselves to the new mother, especially the first-time mother. Women vary tremendously in the degree of difficulty they encounter in the transition from being pregnant to being a mother, but the overriding impression given by the survey is of the need for support for the new mother whether in the postnatal ward or after she gets home. Very often she never receives such support.

Denise, from Cheshire, summed up the feelings of many women about the weeks following the birth of their babies like this:

> *It was silly and unnecessary but I felt I now had to look after a husband, a toddler and a baby and wondered at times who would look after me.*

Becoming a mother is, for some women, a comparatively easy matter. Pregnancy and delivery progress normally, the baby is planned and much looked forward to. The husband is there to give support and help throughout pregnancy, birth and in the early weeks; friends and relatives help with older children, breastfeeding advice is available and within a few weeks mother and baby are happily settled into a routine. For many families this is an intensely happy time. The family come together to welcome in the new baby and to help mother to get back on her feet again. **Sheilagh** is from Northumberland. This baby was her third and any moments of stress or depression she felt soon passed:

> *I didn't need any medical help as my husband cuddled me and told me not to worry as he would help . . . my husband provided the care with his arms and his help.*

Women after birth are emotionally vulnerable and physically drained . . . yet at this very moment they have to take on the daunting task of caring for a baby (something they may know very little about), having constant broken nights whilst also trying to recover their own strength. It is scarcely surprising that the weeks following birth leave many women feeling completely exhausted and sometimes very depressed. A little tender loving care and a lot of practical help can make all the difference between a fulfilled and relaxed mother or a miserable and tense one. This chapter is all about 'caring for the carer'. Just as a few weeks of good medical care can save a sick new baby from a lifetime of handicap, so a few weeks of cosseting and support can create lifelong happiness between mother and child.

Master/Miss Average *That's Life* 1981 baby

The average *That's Life* baby weighed 3,400 grams (7lb 8oz). If he was a boy (51 per cent) he weighed 3,450 grams (7lb 10oz). If she was a girl she weighed 3,340 grams (7lb 6oz) – 10 grams less. Nearly forty per cent of all *That's Life* babies weighed between 3,000 grams and 3,500 grams (6lb 10oz and 7lb 11oz).

The most popular time of day for Master/Miss Average *That's Life* baby to be born was between 12.00 and 1.00 p.m. in the afternoon (318 babies). The least popular time of day was between 10.00 p.m. and 1.00 a.m. (3 per cent for each hour). As we saw in the previous chapter, 81 per cent of babies were born after labours lasting less than twelve hours.

That's Life babies were more likely to be born in the late morning and afternoon than at any other time of the day or night. Nearly a third were born between 11.00 a.m. and 5.00 p.m. With a third having been induced the result was more babies arriving in the middle of the day (following early morning inductions). Most hospitals do induce women in the morning so that deliveries take place when the maximum number of staff are on duty.

More *That's Life* babies were born on a Friday than any other day (923 babies). Sunday was certainly the day of rest as far as deliveries go. Only 615 babies were born on Sunday. Fewer inductions take place at the weekend because staffing levels are generally lower.

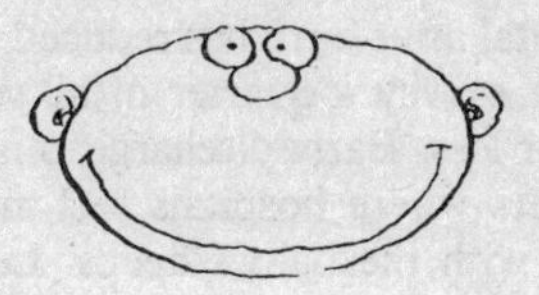

The postnatal ward

The postnatal ward can be a happy and relaxed place where mother and baby get to know each other, where rules scarcely exist, where breastfeeding advice is readily available and where mother can enjoy a few days of being looked after before she goes home. Sadly, it seems that this idyllic picture is all too rare.

A happy and relaxed atmosphere is more commonly found in small maternity units, many of which are now threatened with closure. In these units better staffing levels and less pressure creates a nursing home atmosphere which women find much more appropriate in the days following delivery. The atmosphere, by contrast, in a large hospital ward, despite the best endeavours of some medical staff, is all too often the very reverse of what most women need after having a baby. Staff are rushed, facilities are overloaded, rest is impossible with doctors' rounds taking precedence over a newly delivered woman's greatest desire – to sleep, and feeding times can be laid down for the hospital's, not the woman's convenience.

We *have* heard from women, however, who had happy and restful stays in large hospitals, so it clearly can be done, but on the whole the women who left hospital most refreshed were those who either delivered in or were transferred to smaller units. It would be regrettable if the trend towards the closure of these units continues. Apart from providing for the delivery of low-risk women, they also have a most valuable role to play in the postnatal period.

In country areas a woman who does not wish to return home

after a forty-eight-hour stay can prolong her hospital stay by moving to one of these units if there is one in her area. This brings her closer to her family and friends while giving her more rest than seems possible in a big hospital. Expensive hospital beds are also vacated, reducing pressure and rush for those women who have to stay there.

The stay in hospital after birth has reduced steadily during the last decade. In our survey a quarter of all women stayed only forty-eight hours or less. Early discharge is more common with second-time mothers where hospitals feel more confident that mother is familiar with the baby's needs. Less than a third of mothers spent more than six days in hospital. These women tended to have had Caesarians, to be first-time mothers or to have babies who were in need of continuing medical attention.

A trend during the past decade which has met with widespread approval is that which has brought babies closer to their mothers in the postnatal ward. Forty per cent of *That's Life* women had their babies with them all the time in the days after delivery, and only 3 per cent none of the time. Those women who did report being separated from their babies for 'any length of time' gave rest as the reason in 56 per cent of cases. However, there was a significant percentage (26 per cent) who said they were separated from their babies because of 'hospital routine'.

Some hospitals are still old fashioned in their approach to the 'lying-in period'. Feed times are four hours apart, and babies go to the nurseries at the very least at night and in some cases most of the day as well. Other hospitals go to the other extreme and allow total freedom of choice – mothers feed when they wish, and when their babies wish, and keep their babies by them (or in their beds) as and when they wish.

It is by no means universal for women to approve this latter pattern. It is interesting to read of so many women saying that they did not want babies in the ward at night. Mindful of their imminent return home and night feeds to come, many women were grateful for undisturbed nights.

Women particularly liked the arrangement where babies stayed in the nursery at night and mothers were woken to feed their babies. But, still the clear message is that each woman knows what suits her and her baby best.

New mothers want to be asked whether they want to have

their baby at night or not and for the ward to be arranged so that real choice is a possibility.

The quotes that follow are typical of some of the more positive comments we received on postnatal wards. **Gillian**, from Abbey Wood in London, reported:

At Greenwich they are very free and easy. Baby was put in the nursery at night only if you felt you needed a rest, otherwise baby was with you all the time.

Another **Gillian** from London found arrangements very satisfactory:

All mothers were given the choice on the first night as to whether they had their babies or not. I think this is very fair and personally as I wanted to breastfeed I kept her with me from birth.

Lyndis, from Boston in Lincolnshire, is a personnel assistant:

She was taken away for the first six evenings so I could rest but it was entirely up to me. I was always asked. During the day and evening she was always with me and I was able to bath and change and feed her from the second day onwards.

Angela is from Canterbury:

I had freedom to do as I thought necessary for my baby and myself. I took the baby to the nursery for the night before I came home to get a full night's sleep.

Hilary, from High Wycombe, is a teacher:

I was able to have Gillian with me or in the nursery as I wished. To begin with I was really pleased to be able to have her with me – that was the time I really needed the contact. I could even have her in my room when she was having phototherapy which I thought was very good.

Sian, from Bayswater, is twenty. She had her baby at the West London Hospital which was one of the first British hospitals to pioneer a natural approach to childbirth:

I was tired at first but the baby was allowed to sleep in bed with me. I wasn't interfered with at all.

Pamela is from Sheffield:

I felt better having Lisa with me all the time. This way I could reassure myself that she was all right at any time. Also, I found I was very possessive with her in hospital and needed to have her nearby.

Ann is from Worcester. She contrasted two types of postnatal ward:

The baby was with me most of the time – which was lovely as when my first child was born I only saw him at feeding times. This was much nicer and I felt I knew my daughter so much better when I brought her home from the hospital.

These women were glad to be able to have their baby cared for at night. **Jill** was particularly grateful that the staff realized that she needed extra help. She had been transferred from a GP unit as an emergency and after a long labour (her baby was wedged against the pelvis) had a forceps delivery:

I was grateful in a way that the baby was in the nursery during the night as, not feeling at all well, I do not think I could have managed with having the baby with me all the time. I believe the staff understood this and helped as much as possible.

Janet is from Kidlington in Oxfordshire:

My baby was with me in the four-bedded ward all day and then we put our babies in the nursery adjoining the ward at night. I felt this was a very good arrangement and meant that I got used to dealing with our baby right from birth. Most of the time you had to get on with looking after your baby yourself. If you had any doubt as to what to do you rang for a nurse and they were always very helpful and patient. They spent as much time with you as you needed. The nursing staff woke me at night when baby needed feeding if I did not hear him crying and then I fed him in the nursery.

Susan is from Bexhill on Sea:

I felt good as I could pick her up when I wanted and give her a cuddle and know I would not be moaned at by the nurses.

Small maternity units received much praise.

Glynis from St Austell had her baby in Truro and she was then transferred back to the maternity unit in St Austell. Apart from her feeling that transport should have been provided for her for the transfer, she was happy with her care, particularly at St Austell:

The only thing I have to complain about is fourteen hours after delivery I was asked if I wished to be transferred to the St Austell hospital nearer to home. Fair enough, I said yes. But I had to arrange my own transport. This meant that my baby and I went in my father's car. They cannot provide transport any more, Maggie's cutbacks. I feel that for a fourteen-hours-old baby and mum this was not a very healthy move!

I would like to say how delighted I was with the treatment I received in hospital (especially in St Austell) during my stay. The atmosphere was so relaxed and there was no set time for feeds. You fed as the baby needed it. The staff without exception were kind, helpful, and had terrific senses of humour. I had a lovely week in hospital and I am sure this is one reason why I have no depression whatsoever.

Jane, from Lymington, described clearly the benefits of a small unit for the postnatal stay:

In Southampton the baby remained with you at all times. In the smaller unit they were removed at night, although you still fed at night but the staff came and woke you. I enjoyed my stay at the maternity home and I think there should be more of this type of unit around.

I was lucky that there was one available in this area (and it nearly shut down due to health cuts but public opinion has given it a leave of stay). Only ten beds and two full-time midwives plus other staff. They were very helpful especially when I had my first baby. They helped with breastfeeding (which I feel I might have given up without their help). They made you feel that no problem was too small. I feel it is a great shame that these small units are being threatened with closure when they can give you such a good start to a close relationship with your child and also help your husband accept the change in the family.

Christine, from Haslingden in Lancashire, also enjoyed being in a small unit:

My husband and I cannot fault the care and attention I was given in the small unit. In fact, I asked to be transferred back after the birth and was allowed to do this when the baby was two days old. I felt more relaxed and able to cope better once I was transferred. I would not like to spend a full week in the larger hospital despite its superior facilities.

Some women did comment on their unhappy stay in hospital after the birth of their babies; and in particular about rigid routines. **Jane** is from Luton:

The baby was given to you from 5.30 a.m. onwards for feeds and then taken back to the nursery. Otherwise he was left at the end of the bed but we were not encouraged to get to know them. If they started to cry they were whisked away. It left you feeling very lonely and incompetent.

Alison, from Dudley, wrote:

. . . the hospital routine of four hourly feeds was difficult to keep to. Towards the end I ignored it.

Ann is from Humberside:

. . . at night-time as long as you want to breastfeed your baby they wake you. Other times routine overrides anything else. For example, if the baby is hungry and crying at your meal times it is wheeled away to cry in the nursery.

Gillian, from Nottinghamshire, told us:

I think it helps mother and baby bonding if the baby is with mum all the time. The staff took my baby away one night because he would not take his feed and I cried all night.

Carol is from Milton Keynes. The picture she draws of her postnatal ward is not a happy one . . . at least not for the mothers, fathers and babies:

When you have just had a baby you should be left to get to know it. I was told off for talking to our son. If our babies cried in between feeds they were put into the nursery, even at visiting times when the husbands were there.

Pamela, from Warwickshire, is a hotel accountant, and seemed to accept that hospitals cannot allow mothers to be with their babies all the time:

I would have liked the baby with me all the time although this is not always practical in hospitals. It almost felt like having a doll to play with during the day but to be put back in the 'toy box' at night.

Margaret found the staff unsympathetic to her need to have her baby near her:

I was very frustrated immediately following the delivery because I was confined to bed and the baby was in the nursery at the end of the ward. Babies were crying and I did not know if mine was, but I could not go and see. The only solution offered by the sister was a Mogadon tablet (for me, not the baby).

Mothers with babies in special care units can feel very desolate when they are surrounded by mothers with healthy babies.

Janet, from Eastbourne, is an accounts clerk:

Three other mums in the same room had their babies with them and I felt the odd one out as mine was in special care.

Other similar problems that arose stemmed from women feeling left out for other reasons. **Pauline**, from Studley, is eighteen:

In hospital I wanted to get up because I felt lonely as I was the youngest in the ward and the others couldn't talk to me like they could with each other.

Many women pointed out that nurses and midwives were too

busy to give help and advice and how much this was missed. **Lavinia**, from Basingstoke, is a teacher:

I was exhausted and disappointed that nursing isn't more helpful and kind, especially when you are in great pain and totally tired – having to do everything for yourself – even getting in and out of bed is tiring and extremely painful.

Where there is a shortage of staff, and midwives in particular, time is just not available for the kind of patient and sympathetic help which almost all first-time mothers, and many second-time mothers, need. **Gillian**, a first-time mother from Essex, suffered from a lack of this kind of help, as well as a serious shortage of supplies:

The postnatal treatment was diabolical. Like many others this was my first baby but we were not given any help, advice or encouragement. Things were so bad – there was no salt for the bath. I had to phone my husband to bring me iron tablets as the hospital did not have any. I finally telephoned my mother in tears at 11.15 p.m. and begged her to fetch me because I could not stand it any more. I came out of hospital not even knowing how to put a nappy on my baby.

This was a description of a major London teaching hospital.

Shortage of facilities *and* beds was also acute in **Barbara's** hospital in West Yorkshire:

The nurses on the ward asked me politely if I would vacate my bed two days early and go home with the baby because they were desperately short of beds!

Barbara had two other children and had suffered from exhaustion during her pregnancy.

Susan had perhaps the most unhappy stay in a postnatal ward of any revealed by our survey. Fortunately, it was not typical. Her journey to the postnatal ward started with a broken lift:

The lift had broken down, so I was back in the labour ward with my baby for a couple of hours.

I was in great pain and had difficulty in lifting the baby out of her cot, changing the nappy etc. but there was nobody to help or to tell me when to breastfeed or help with that either.

We were supposed to have two salt baths a day but there was no salt during the time I was in the hospital. The food was inedible and I lived on whatever my husband could bring in.

My baby screamed for four days and nights almost without stopping (very embarrassing when twenty-five other mums and babies are trying to sleep). She was a fairly big baby and was very hungry. My milk did not come for four days but it was hospital policy not to allow her even a drink of water because she was going to be breastfed.

Lindsay came up in big red blotches all over her body especially under the arms. I complained to a doctor and a sister who said that it was caused by the starch in the hospital linen. I said surely they didn't starch the baby things but she said it was hospital policy to starch everything.

On the third night the central heating failed and the temperature on the ward dropped to sixty degrees during the night, so gradually one by one we trundled our babies down to the nursery where it was still warm. By morning there were fifteen babies crammed into a nursery designed to have only three at one time. I had to lend the girl in the next bed a jersey to wear as it was so cold. This continued through day four and on day five they decided to send as many of us home or to other hospitals as possible. I went home although I felt dreadful. I just couldn't wait to get away from the hospital.

Lindsay was not bathed until the day we came home, and then only because I insisted. The nurse 'discovered' a strange ridge under her left arm, although I had been complaining about the spots on her body. The paediatrician was called and said it looked like scar tissue but she didn't know from what, but to keep an eye on it and tell my GP. When we had been home for five days it developed into a large abscess and spread round onto her back, so we had to go into the children's hospital for two days.

Although I felt ill when I got home it was a relief to be under the care of my midwife and GP.

I worried so much about everything that I lost my milk and gave up breastfeeding after four weeks.

All in all, what I expected to be a joyful, fulfilling experience, was painful, degrading, frightening and upsetting.

It all seems a terrible tale of woe, but I was not the only woman in the hospital to feel like this.

A postnatal ward can be a source of stress and exhaustion to women and their new babies. But, as we have seen, there were women in our survey who had happy reports of their stay in hospital; babies were with their mothers most of the time, sometimes sharing her bed; the nursery was there if mother needed a restful night or an afternoon nap; friendly and expert staff were available in sufficient numbers to give emotional and practical support when required. Women who were fortunate enough to stay in such a postnatal ward came home more refreshed and ready to cope than other less fortunate mothers. Small maternity units were particularly successful at providing this kind of postnatal care.

Hale and hearty?

More than twenty per cent of *That's Life* babies were reported as having had serious problems during labour and delivery but given that these problems were swiftly and expertly seen to, only relatively few babies were reported as still not being healthy at birth (5 per cent). These included babies with congenital abnormalities as well as premature and 'growth-retarded' babies. It is an interesting finding of this survey that 2 per cent of mothers reported that their babies were not given a check-up after birth. How many dislocated hips or heart murmurs escaped identification? Are babies delivered at home less likely to be checked by a doctor? They are certainly less likley to be checked by a specialist in baby disorders.

Twelve per cent of all *That's Life* babies spent some time in a special or intensive care unit. Mothers of babies who needed special care were full of appreciation for doctors, nurses and midwives who not only cared for their babies, but also took time to explain what the problems were. Childbirth alone is a stressful and exhausting business but when it is combined with anxiety

about the health of the baby the weeks following birth can be a nightmare. The difference that patient and comprehensive discussion can make is clear. The other message to come from mothers whose babies had to be in special care is the misery that can result from sharing a ward with mothers whose babies are hale and hearty. To be in a side room, or a room next to the special care unit can lessen the sense of 'why me?'

A welcoming unit with open visiting for parents and children was very important in helping parents to feel loving towards their baby.

There were slightly fewer small babies (born too soon, or too small) in our survey than the official national figure. Five per cent of the babies in our survey weighed less than 2,500 grams (5lb 8oz) compared with 7.3 per cent which is the official figure. The difference is mainly accounted for by the social class and age bias of our survey. As we have seen, mothers under twenty-one had more than twice the number of small babies (11 per cent) compared with the figure for mothers as a whole (5 per cent). However, women under twenty-one were less likely to respond to the survey than were older women and this helps to explain why we had fewer small babies in our survey than the national figure.

Some of the most touching and triumphant stories in our survey came from the one per cent of women whose babies weighed less than 1,500 grams (3lb 5oz) and were saved by expert care. Deep appreciation was expressed not just for the care these babies received but especially for the kindness and sympathy the parents themselves received from staff. This helped mothers and fathers immensely in not losing contact with their tiny babies and in recovering from their difficult ordeal.

The smallest baby born to any woman in our survey and still alive when the survey was completed was Amy, daughter of **Tricia**, from Romsey in Hampshire. Amy weighed 800 grams (1lb 12oz). Tricia's first baby was born at twenty-nine weeks and died after fifteen hours because of immature lungs. Tricia received excellent antenatal care during her second pregnancy, seeing the consultant every week from six weeks of pregnancy. She spent five weeks in hospital (from nine to fourteen weeks pregnancy). She says:

On every visit to the consultant or GP I was made to feel special – everyone was determined that this pregnancy should be successful!

She was allowed to take a video recording of the scan (she had five). Despite personal efforts by the consultant to stop labour at twenty-five weeks she delivered her baby. She was told the baby had a 2 per cent chance of survival. She was delivered by the consultant who was:

. . . very sympathetic and could not have given greater care.

Amy – her baby – was extremely premature – fifteen weeks early – but was healthy considering her age. She had the usual problems of immaturity: weakness of lungs, too small to feed orally, open heart valve, inability to produce red blood cells – otherwise perfect. **Tricia** describes her feelings:

Very lost . . . I couldn't believe that Amy could live more than a few hours, the other babies looked fat and unreal, a different species. I felt I shouldn't be on a postnatal ward . . . I cry every few days. But I would say this is a build-up of stress not postnatal depression . . . the staff of the SCBU have gone out of their way to help and understand us. We have been allowed to visit Amy any hour of day and night and take endless photographs . . . Amy is now seven weeks old and her weight is 960 grams. She has had many problems with ventilation, infection, anaemia, and collapsing lungs. However, throughout she has remained lively and determined, a real character and a favourite of special care staff at Southampton for whom she is a record at twenty-five weeks' gestation at birth. She is now the equivalent of thirty-two weeks' gestation and today is breathing for herself without ventilation and taking milk at two mls per hour through a nasal gastric tube.*†

* Special Care Baby Unit.

† Amy is now seven months old. She came out of hospital after sixteen weeks in intensive care. She is the smallest baby ever to have survived from this intensive care unit (Southampton). She now weighs 8½lb, and is an entirely normal, healthy and lovely baby.

Hilary is a physiotherapist from Cheltenham. She had an abruption of the placenta at thirty-two weeks which meant the baby's lifeline was cut off.

I awoke at 4.00 a.m. with bleeding and called the GP who sent me to hospital. My husband took me in the car. I also developed toxaemia following the placental bleeding so I had an emergency Caesarian . . . Being such a small size [2lb 14oz] there was a paediatrician present . . . She developed grunting [breathing problems] and to be on the safe side she was tranferred to Bristol SCBU . . . I saw her briefly after I came round and then she was transferred to Bristol. I could not follow because of my high blood pressure . . . I very much enjoyed having her back with me when she returned to Cheltenham SCBU.

The day after she was transferred the paediatrician came and told me everything that had happened and discussed the whole problem of her future care.

Yvonne had her baby at the John Radcliffe Hospital, Oxford:

The baby was two months early and could not breathe on his own as his lungs were not working properly. The doctor came and talked to us about what was wrong with him and about all the different machines he was on.

I would just like to add a thank you to the staff on the special care baby unit as they were so good. There were toys that the other children could play with to keep them amused while you were seeing to the baby, plus they have a parents room where you can make yourself a drink, which they supply. If you had any problems you could really feel you could talk to them. They also made you feel your baby was special and not just another baby.

Rosemary's baby was born at thirty-six weeks, following her high blood pressure and the baby's 'high' position. Her baby, Abigail, was in special care for nearly two weeks:

The baby was born at thirty-six weeks and was immediately put in an incubator because of respiratory problems. Immediately I came to after the Caesarian, the baby was given to me and I was told that he was going into an incubator. I was kept fully informed throughout. The following morning the staff took me in a wheelchair to see my baby.

I did suffer depression, but I cannot say it was specifically postnatal. Rather connected to the problems the baby had and particularly her being in the SCBU and not knowing for how long, and me being at home without her and not knowing when she would be home with us.

Patricia, from Chippenham, is a teacher. Her daughter, Hannah, was in special care for nearly two weeks:

My waters broke prematurely (five weeks early) so I went to my local maternity hospital where I was examined. From there I was sent to Bath Hospital because of the likelihood of a premature birth. [She weighed 4lb 4oz.] She was placed in an incubator from birth to maintain body heat and later developed jaundice and was given phototherapy. The hospital staff were most sympathetic and kind and discussed my baby's progress openly. I knew that Hannah was in the best place possible and I was allowed to see her any time and also encouraged to feed and change her. But, I felt envious of the mums who had their babies at their bedside.

Gwendolyn is from St Albans. Her first baby had suffered from a blood problem as well as having a dislocation of the hips, and had spent some time in special care. Her second son, Adrian, also needed special care. Like Patricia, she was transferred (at thirty-seven weeks) from a GP unit to St Albans City Hospital following her waters breaking:

He was premature and jaundiced but very healthy apart from this. He was put under phototherapy and I was well informed by staff as I knew them all well in special care due to my first baby. Concern was given to me because of this as my thoughts returned to my first baby.

Anne is a household management executive. Her second baby had to have a blood transfusion because of Rhesus incompatibility. For this reason Anne was transferred to the University Hospital of Wales at twenty-four weeks pregnancy. The first hospital had failed to give her the necessary anti-D immunization after her first baby was born. She found the University Hospital very helpful:

My baby was taken away immediately after delivery for a blood transfusion. I held her for a minute before. The treatment was discussed fully with my husband and I beforehand. I was quite content knowing she was safe in the special care unit and I could see her there at any time. They were always busy but always made me welcome.

Sheila, from South West London, found the reserves of strength to cope with a very worrying time, and was especially grateful to friends and hospital staff:

The second day Oliver was home he did not seem 'normal'. I took him to Westminster Children's Hospital. After tests it was discovered he had had a brain haemorrhage – probably at birth. He was also having fits. He was in intensive care and the staff were exemplary.

He is now taking phenabarbitone and epilin to control the fits but it is too early to say how the brain damage will affect him.

His progress to date is good and it is possible that another part of the brain will take over the function of the damaged part and he could *grow up to be quite normal. Time will tell.*

Friends and neighbours have been wonderful to us and the hospital very supportive.

I was shattered and felt very cheated (as my eldest son was born with a hole in the heart). But, it is amazing what strength you find when you need it.

Linda, from Birmingham, lost her very premature baby. The baby was not transferred to a highly specialized unit although she weighed only 992 grams (2lb 3oz):

My baby was born premature by Caesarian at twenty-eight weeks because it was getting distressed inside me. The hospital had explained to my husband and me that the baby's lungs might not be developed enough for it to survive . . . I suffered some depression which was mainly due to having my baby die twenty-two hours after birth because her lungs were not quite strong enough.

Christine, from Stockport, also lost her baby because of prematurity:

I was taken to hospital suffering from a haemorrhage. I was kept in hospital for two weeks and consideration was then being given to my discharge. But then my waters broke unexpectedly and I went into early labour.

My baby son was born eleven weeks premature. He died eighteen hours later. He was extremely premature and there were problems with his breathing because his lungs were so weak and under-developed. He was immediately taken to the special care unit after delivery. I was told he had died first and had to break the news to my husband, which wasn't a very easy thing to do.

I was devastated by the loss of our baby son . . . tearful and depressed. A sense of failure, especially to my husband.

After Christine went home she wrote:

The midwife called regularly. The health visitor called on two occasions. The National Childbirth telephoned and asked if I would like someone to call round to talk to. I accepted. I had paid for mothercraft classes which I was not able to attend. I am very fortunate to have an extremely happy marriage and couldn't wish for a more loving and considerate husband.

Some mothers whose babies spent time in a special care unit found staff less helpful. **Marilyn**, from Redditch, for example:

He was born three weeks premature and went into special care after three days with a high level of jaundice. A nurse came to take him away with hardly any explanation. I was in quite a state of shock. Eventually a doctor explained but I went through a lot of unnecessary pain and anguish by not being told by a doctor earlier. I thought it was the end of the world that day and got very depressed and tearful.

Sara, from West London, wrote:

My baby was four-and-a-half weeks premature and could not breathe unassisted. She later proved to have a serious handicap – bilateral vocal cord paralysis – and at the age of five weeks had to have a tracheostomy. No one discussed her condition with me for two days.

She describes her feelings as:

Frightened, lonely, isolated. Scared that the baby would die and unable to really voice that question 'will she live?'

Elaine is from Cheshire, and she. too, felt isolated after the birth of her baby:

A few days after, she had chest problems. She was slightly jaundiced and had suspected clicking hips. I was very distressed as no one bothered with me, the mother. I wish there had been someone who had got the time to sit and discuss these problems in such a delicate situation.

She was in special care for four days. The only way I could get there at first was by wheelchair and only at feed time. When I got there, they had already fed her and I was supposed to be breastfeeding. Their attitude was appalling.

Lea, from Norwich, is a bacteriologist. This was her first baby:

I was not booked into the main hospital but contractions started whilst at my leaving party at work. I was thirty-three weeks pregnant. I went home and telephoned my husband. He rang the doctor who told my husband to take me to the main hospital straight away.

The baby weighed 5lb 5oz. He was:

Seven weeks premature. He had a temperature problem and became badly jaundiced. He was taken away from me and nobody would tell me how he was when I was taken down to the ward.

I was the only mother without her baby and I felt very depressed and hurt, and anxious about the baby.

She described her feelings as:

Desperately alone and tired and absolutely incapable of coping – only sometimes though.

It was not only mothers whose babies had to stay in the special care unit who needed reassurance and explanation about their babies. **Linda** from Bradford's baby was a breech birth:

His head was out of shape due to use of forceps and his hip was clicking slightly. No one told us about either until I asked what the words 'skull? Abnormal shape' meant on his notes the night after. Then I had to look into it myself. Still they never told me about his hip.

A nurse from a different ward came and explained to me that babies born breech often have a misshaped head. Also the young nurses who were training were more helpful than some of the older ones. Plus, of course, my husband was as helpful as possible, but not knowing any more than I did, what could he do?

However good our medical services are and however healthy our women are, babies will still be born needing expert care if they are to develop into normal, healthy children. However, the strain and stress for parents of a sick newborn baby are enormous. Medical staff, friends and relations *can* turn a potentially agonizing few days or weeks into an experience which brings mother and father closer to each other and to their child, and better able to take the responsibility for their baby when it is fit enough to come home.

Breastfeeding – doing what comes naturally?

Breastfeeding can be an intensely rewarding experience, both for mother and baby. A unique intimacy comes from being able to supply your own baby with all its needs – a natural continuation of the nine months of pregnancy when the growing baby derives all its needs from its mother. What can compare with the look of satisfied contentment on a baby's face as it falls asleep at its mother's breast after a feed? And, what can compare with a mother's feeling of deep fulfilment at such moments?

The last decade has seen a tremendous increase in breastfeeding. As the nutritional, emotional and medical advantages of breast milk over powdered milk have become better understood, more and more women have at least tried to breastfeed although sadly they have all too often had to give up. Any woman who had a baby in the early 1970s and again in the later part of the decade will probably have noticed a tremendous shift in medical attitudes towards breastfeeding. Ten years ago ward routine revolved around the four hourly bottle feeds, a trolley would appear on the stroke of 2, 6, 10, day and night, and bottles would be dished out to the waiting mothers and hungry babies.

Now, at least in the more progressive units, a very different atmosphere prevails. There is scarcely a bottle to be seen, babies are with their mothers all day and night (if the mother wishes it) and mother and baby can work out for themselves what pattern of feeding works best. This usually settles down to frequent feeds in the early days and weeks gradually changing into a pattern of wider apart, bigger feeds as the baby grows. Night-time feeds are frequent to start with and slowly disappear as the baby can absorb more food in the daytime (and especially in the evening).

Demand feeding is the name given to this approach to infant feeding and its increasing popularity has resulted in many more mothers establishing successful breastfeeding. Eighty-three per cent of our mothers started breastfeeding compared with 51 per cent in 1975*. It also results in much quieter postnatal wards. The awful sound of miserable, hungry babies which dominated the postnatal ward as feed time approached is fortunately mostly a thing of the past. Animals in the zoo may be fed on rigid timetables, but no one would suggest that this should be applied to animals who are nursing their young. We have learnt that nature knows best and that breastfeeding, if it is to be successful, evolves through the relationship of mother to baby and baby to mother not through the imposition of rules and routines.

Sadly breastfeeding does not come easily to a large number of women. Breastfeeding may be the natural thing to do but it

* 'Breastfeeding' (DHSS) 1978 HMSO.

still needs to be worked at and learnt, and without the right kind of help at the right time, many women will give up out of sheer exhaustion, pain and frustration.

Eighty-three per cent of *That's Life* mothers started breastfeeding their babies. Within four weeks nearly twenty per cent of these had stopped. And after four weeks roughly two thirds of all mothers were still breastfeeding. This compares with only 24 per cent after six weeks in 1975. Of those who stopped breastfeeding, over half (53 per cent) said it was because they had trouble doing it. Since 43 per cent of women reported receiving no help with breastfeeding, it is perhaps scarcely surprising that a fifth of women gave up. It seems a shame that 82 per cent of women reported being encouraged to breastfeed and yet 43 per cent received no actual help to do so.

Comments from women on breastfeeding ranged widely from those who felt unstinting gratitude to midwives, mothers or friends who spent *time* in the early weeks helping them to overcome problems of engorgement, sore nipples or failing milk supply to those women who suffered great physical pain and discomfort and could not find anyone to help them. Help which is available but not 'for three hours' can be too late for an already fed-up and worried mother who is close to feeling 'it's just not worth all this trouble'.

The strong impression from comments sent us about breastfeeding is that most women want to breastfeed but that the quality and type of advice they receive in the early weeks is critical to their success in doing so.

For some women breastfeeding comes easily, the baby is put to the breast immediately after birth and mother and baby never look back. 'It was just so natural' . . . 'no problems whatsoever' . . . 'my mother breastfed me and I just assumed it would be easy and it was'. These mothers may have a little soreness or a few hours of engorgement to contend with but once the first week or two has passed, breastfeeding just seems easy and natural. For other mothers, and especially those having their first baby, the course of nature was not so smooth. But given the right help at the right time a tricky few days or weeks were successfully dealt with and breastfeeding was soundly established.

These women needed help to breastfeed and were lucky

enough to find it when they needed it. **Ruth**, from Belfast, was typical:

It was much more difficult to establish than I realized and but for the sister in my ward in hospital I would never have succeeded. On occasions she spent two hours with me helping me and coaxing the baby to breastfeed. I am glad that I have succeeded as I feel the baby is much more contented and getting a good start in life.

Brenda, from Clywd:

Dreadful pain at first, nearly gave up. The sisters in Chatsworth were marvellous and helpful. Really gave me all the encouragement I needed. I am fine now and enjoying doing it.

Yvonne, from Nottinghamshire, also found help was there when she wanted it:

The district midwife was extremely helpful especially when I thought I hadn't enough milk. She reassured me that I did have enough and we have been fine since. Also received plenty of help with first few feeds in hospital. Often the nurses would sit with me throughout the feed.

Alicia, from Enfield:

The baby wakes every 2½ to three hours for feeds. One of my nipples was sore and cracked but my midwife advised me to use Rotosept spray and said they could loan me a pump to express if I needed. She gave me encouragement which I was glad of as I could have given up breastfeeding because of the discomfort.

Elizabeth, from Tidworth in Hampshire, is a chiropodist:

Midwife was invaluable at home. She insisted on demand feeding which was discouraged at the hospital. She encouraged me to do so, even feeding every hour or so to begin with.

Many women who did not find the right kind of help in hospital found it either through friends and relations or through the National Childbirth Trust counselling service. Some women found it easier to learn from a 'friendly person at home' and especially so when such a person had breastfed herself and knew that it was not always easy. Books were also a great help – *Breast is Best** received many commendations. **Kay**, from Wigan struggled for three months before finding the NCT and *Breast is Best*:

> *I had great problems in the early weeks due to lack of knowledge about the subject. I struggled for three months before finally contacting a breastfeeding counsellor (NCT) who advised me to read a book about breastfeeding (*Breast is Best*) and from that moment on my problem no longer existed.*

Charlotte, from Ipswich, wrote:

> *The midwives made the baby and me very tired and made me sore and I felt bruised. Henry just screamed and screamed with the midwife's hand grasped around his neck shoving his straining head on to my sore breast. My mother-in-law, who is a midwife, stayed a full twenty-four hours with me and was marvellous in establishing breastfeeding.*

Elizabeth, from Sutherland, found her sister helpful:

> *I could not get him to fix for several days and the only help I was given was the nurses yanking my nipple, squeezing out some colostrum and shoving it in the baby's mouth. Eventually my sister suggested a different position when I put him to the breast. This worked immediately and has never failed me since.*

Some women just wanted to be left alone and not be bothered by well-meaning helpers. And, certainly not by hospital routines (not always so easy). **Linda**, from York:

> *I fed my first baby only for four weeks as I was engorged the whole time. This time I am following my own instinct (*not *hospital routine) and feed Hannah whenever she's unsettled. I have been very successful and she gained 2lb 10oz in three weeks.*

Hospitals which give bottles to babies whom mothers are breast-

* *Breast is Best* by Andrew Stanway, Pan Books, 1978.

feeding met with disapproval. **Patricia**, from Halifax, succeeded in breastfeeding with her third baby:

I breastfed my first for four weeks and then stopped because the baby was always crying. Second baby I fed for six weeks but stopped because my nipples were sore. This time I am doing fine because my baby was not given a bottle at the hospital before I fed her. I firmly believe this is the reason for my success this time.

All these reports were from women who were still happily breastfeeding their babies at least four weeks after birth. For one in five mothers who started breastfeeding the outcome was not so happy. For various reasons women found it easier to give up. Lack of advice or conflicting advice seems to be a major reason why these breastfeeding mothers stopped. Good advice and support at the right time can, as we have seen, enable women to overcome even the most difficult problems. Seventeen per cent of women who gave up said it was for 'health reasons' and 16 per cent said it was their 'own wish' to stop.

Jennifer is a health visitor but even with her training, she felt the need for help:

I had a lot of theoretical knowledge but still felt I needed help and support. Between the seven and fourteen day period help and support in hospital were non-existent.

Evelyn, from Romford, might have carried on breastfeeding if the right help had been available. But it might also be that mothers who do not really want to breastfeed (perhaps because of previous difficulties) are inclined to believe that they stopped for other reasons. There certainly is a feeling amongst some women, that they *ought* to breastfeed and that deciding to stop breastfeeding is a 'failure' both in their own eyes and in the eyes of the hospital:

I stopped breastfeeding almost before I began! I put my baby to the breast but he would not suck. I had no effective help and waited over two hours for somebody to help me, by which time I had gone off the whole idea (I had previously fed my first child for seven weeks which I did not particularly enjoy) and so I decided to bottle feed.

Wendy, from Wimbourne in Dorset, felt more time spent with an adviser would have prevented her 'giving up':

If more time was spent with me to help master feeding I think we both could have taken to it. Matthew got very upset which in turn upset me.

Brenda, from Woking, had an experience which suggests an extraordinary lack of understanding on the part of the nursery nurse:

One of the nursery nurses helped me once in hospital. Because the baby was asleep and it was feedtime she tried forcefully ramming him on the breast which I disliked and then came back twenty minutes later and tut-tutted because he was still on the same side.

Sheryl, from Sussex, was advised that colic would be reduced by changing to the bottle. The *cost* was the only change she noticed:

I was advised to stop feeding the baby as he had colic badly. They told me that I had too much milk and the flow was too fast, making the baby gulp too much air. There was no difference when he was on the bottle except being on the bottle was very expensive.

However, **Dianne** suffered from a regime which was perhaps *over*-inclined towards breastfeeding:

I hoped to breastfeed but found it difficult and I did not produce any milk. I was concerned that my baby was not getting any food but this idea was rejected by the staff who told me to continue and refused to give me dextrose to prevent dehydration (the baby had lost fourteen ounces by the fourth day and was jaundiced).

Alison, from Dudley, summed up well the conflicting advice that can be given to new mothers:

Encouragement without help leads not only to a feeling that it will be straightforward but can also result in a profound sense of failure should breastfeeding not work.

Joyce, from Hounslow, wrote:

When I gave up breastfeeding due to a vicious circle of tiredness and therefore being unable to produce milk, I was treated extremely coldly by the medical staff who intimated by their manner that I was a 'failure' who did not try hard enough.

Nineteen per cent of *That's Life* mothers were bottle-feeding when they returned their surveys (usually four weeks after delivery). Roughly half of these had tried to breastfeed and stopped. For many of these women after a day or a week of struggle it was a great relief to change to the bottle. For others a previous bad experience led them to bottle-feed from the start. **Diana**, a teacher from Swindon, gave a typical account of switching from breast to bottle:

I really wanted to breastfeed because I thought bottle-feeding would be a lot more trouble and bother but in fact I found exactly the opposite. I found breastfeeding exceedingly difficult and painful. My breasts got terribly sore and it was very painful when the baby sucked. My breasts were very full of milk and I found it uncomfortable to be in any other position than on my back.

In the end, the sister advised me to stop breastfeeding because the baby could not take the milk from my nipples very easily despite the fact that I had a lot of milk. So, on the seventh day I bottle-fed and I have been much happier doing so, but I did feel a failure because I was unable to breastfeed.

Breast is best for many, but not for all. If breastfeeding comes naturally and help is available if problems arise then a contented mother and baby is usually the result. If, however, 'nature's course' is too paved with obstacles or if the desire to do it simply is not there, then bottle-feeding will work better. However, it is sad to conclude that there are still many mothers who would dearly love to breastfeed successfully (or 'sucksessfully' as one mother put it) but who cannot find the right person at the right time with the right knowledge to see them through the early difficulties and into a happy and fulfilling breastfeeding relationship with their baby.

Happy days?

Radiant and fulfilled motherhood is an ideal for most pregnant women. Some women in our survey found the weeks after birth full of joy, with few or no difficulties. **Margaret** had experienced postnatal depression with her first baby but with her second (a home delivery) it was a very different story:

> *After my first hospital birth I suffered severe postnatal depression. The whole experience was negative and frightening and took a year to get over. This time because the birth and the postnatal period were such positive experiences, I felt marvellous from the start. Even 6 a.m. starts are a pleasure and my love for my new baby seems more profound and overwhelming. I have more energy and more confidence.*

However, few women did not report some degree of emotional instability in the days and weeks following the birth. Whether they called it four-day blues or the more grandiose postnatal depression or just said 'I felt a bit weepy' it was rare to find a mother who described these early days as entirely wonderful and problem free.

For most women, whether in or out of hospital, the days following birth take them through the whole gamut of human emotions – from the pure ecstasy of having created this new and wonderful baby to the total misery, exhaustion and depression that can follow interrupted nights and a crying baby. But even these feelings were often described in the most positive way . . . 'they were enjoyable tears' . . . 'tears of joy' . . . 'I felt much better for having a good howl'. Women commonly felt miserable for a few minutes or hours and with the help of a comforting shoulder to weep on soon recovered and felt better than before. Those women who could not share these passing feelings and said 'I wish I had someone to talk to' or who were overwhelmed with family or other problems, were more likely to find a passing 'weepiness' turn into something more profound.

Eleven per cent of women who said they suffered postnatal depression said they had 'no one to talk to'.

One other thing is clear, those women who expected the weeks after birth to be 'roses all the way' were less likely to adjust well than women who had a more realistic expectation of life with a new baby and perhaps even some knowledge about the emotional instabilities that can arise postnatally.

The four quotes that follow are typical of many from women describing the 'ups and downs' and the 'happy tears' which affected them. **Denise**, from Cheshire, gave a particularly clear and sensitive account of her feelings:

> *In the first two weeks some days my feelings were a bit like a 'yo yo' . . . over little things. Feeling elated that he was born . . . then tiredness brought me off my cloud with a bump. I did feel a little unimportant in my husband's eyes. It was silly and unnecessary but I felt I now had to look after a husband, a toddler and a baby and wondered at times who would look after me.*

Mary, from Prescot, Merseyside felt:

> *. . . aggressive . . . for the first time in my life I've started smashing cups (and bottles of sauce) around the house. But it's not depression as such.*

Around half of those women who did have 'someone to talk to' found a friend or relative the most helpful. This was usually her husband or partner but quite frequently her mother, sister or neighbour.

However, these feelings of weepiness, the odd bad day or even mild depression must be distinguished from the few cases of 'severe' postnatal depression we heard of. Three per cent of women reported experiencing 'a lot' of postnatal depression. Their descriptions show a clear distinction between those already referred to and a condition which can need treating, either with drugs or as an in-patient in hospital. Some psychiatric hospitals now have special mother and baby units which give sufferers from severe postnatal mental illness the chance to recover without separation from the baby.

Two per cent of women in our survey who suffered from depression received 'professional psychiatric help' and 10 per cent received medication or drug therapy.

GPs, health visitors and midwives are all mentioned by women as being great sources of support at moments of stress. More than a third found either the doctor (7 per cent), midwife or nurse (20 per cent), or health visitor (10 per cent) the 'best person to talk to' about depression. Although as we have seen, the family and friends are 'the best people to talk to' for 50 per cent.

Becoming a mother is such a fundamental change in a woman's life that it is not surprising that it can be the cause of stress, anxiety or depression. Furthermore it is known that a change in the balance of hormones after the birth of a baby can cause an emotional reaction. Those women who are fortunate enough to have supportive husbands, sympathetic families or neighbours, GPs, midwives or health visitors will experience only passing difficulty in coping with such emotions. However, those who lack support may find a few difficult days turning into weeks or even months of stress and exhaustion.

First we look at some quotes from women who did find support. **Lesley** is from Stockport. Her comments were typical:

> *The staff at the hospital said I had the four-day blues. I was happy crying. I couldn't help myself, but they were enjoyable tears.*

Elizabeth, from Brisol, described feeling happy and sad together:

> *It came on after I saw my little boy after a gap of three days. (He was always asleep at visiting time.) It wasn't so much depression as happiness at having two lovely kids.*

Phillipa, from Great Bookham in Surrey, said:

I felt very weepy from about the third day – the slightest thing would trigger the tears but I felt much better for having a good howl.

Jean is forty-two and from Ealing. She felt:

Very bewildered. My youngest is thirteen years – my oldest is twenty-four years. We have three grandchildren. I felt bewildered at the prospect of loving them all the same now there was another little one and the problem seemed insurmountable until I talked it out with my husband.

Jennifer is a telephonist from West Yorkshire. Her twin sons were very premature and both died. She received:

Sympathetic counselling from staff – midwife was very understanding. I needed to talk about it and not ignore the events. My husband has been wonderful and I am very lucky that I have him.

Lynn, from Cleveland, needed some time to herself and then felt better:

After almost three weeks I suddenly started picking arguments with my husband, feeling as if I could not cope, and why did I ever want another one etc. It lasted three days. Then I felt fine again.

Once my husband realized what was wrong he was most sympathetic. Simply by helping me in the house and taking care of the children where and when possible leaving me time to myself. I soon felt better.

Tina lives in Nottinghamshire:

I found my Grandma who visited daily a great help. Just for her being there and having an adult to talk to she really was very good.

Carol is twenty-two and from North West London. She also found a close relative more helpful than a medical staff:

My midwife was sympathetic but I didn't feel that I could talk to her as I didn't know her. My mother was the best person to cry with when I got low.

Jacqueline, from Leicestershire, shared her feelings with a neighbour:

I felt very weepy to begin with but now some tasks seem almost impossible like going to friends for tea. Even going to the next village to shop is an enormity. Our social life has stopped dead and the tiredness is terrible. It gets me down a bit.

A really good moan to my neighbour helps and listening to her problems and comparing notes as to how awkward our husbands are at present. Her daughter was born ten days before Harry.

Carol, from East London, found help from her family and GP:

At first I felt depressed all the time but now, ten days later, it comes over me at certain times of the day. I feel desperately helpless . . . my husband and family were very sympathetic and understanding.

My GP was also very understanding and I did not feel as if I was wasting her time.

Some women found, perhaps, their greatest source of comfort to be someone with no experience or expertise. Both Doreen from Poole and Patricia from Manchester found it was their babies that pulled them through their 'down' moments. First **Doreen**:

As I felt a closer understanding with the baby and knowing I was at least trying to do the best for her helped I believe with depression from the birth and family troubles.

Patricia said:

I felt vaguely depressed for a few weeks, mainly I believe because of having a Caesarian section and dwelling on how I could have done anything to avoid it. The feeling passed as I became more involved in the baby.

GPs, midwives (community mainly) and health visitors were a great source of support to many women when they came home with their new baby. One surprising and encouraging survey finding was the high percentage of women who received home visits in the postnatal period from a GP, midwife and or health visitor.

In fact, 96 per cent of all *That's Life* women were visited by both a midwife and a health visitor and 61 per cent were visited by a GP in the four-week period after delivery. These visits seem to be extremely valuable . . . women find it much easier to discuss their problems whether emotional or physical in their own home. **Louise** is from Hyde in Cheshire:

> *I felt that I just could not cope with anything for a couple of days. My two year old was playing up and I felt like screaming at him and hitting him. It was a horrible feeling. I just wanted to cry all the time. I had no hostile feelings towards the baby though.*
>
> *The midwife and doctor were very good and understanding. My depression only went on for a couple of days but at the time I needed to talk to someone who could reassure me and the midwife, doctor and health visitor were very good.*

Pamela is from Washington:

> *Having been bad with my nerves four years before I was quite scared as I had that same feeling but the doctor really took the time and made me feel that someone cared.*

Lesley, from Newcastle, is a clerical assistant and is twenty-two. She found the hospital midwife helpful:

> *In hospital one night I cried and the staff midwife sat and talked to me for about half-an-hour, about hormone changes etc. and how all new mothers are a bit apprehensive at first.*

Teresa, from Bristol, had an episiotomy which unfortunately was not successful as the stitches did not hold:

> *I get depressed about my own health. I worry about when I can resume a sexual relationship with my husband. I have been told I will not need family planning advice for some time because of my condition.*
>
> *Just to talk helps relieve pent-up feelings. My health visitor has been the most cheering and encouraging friend.*

Sylvia is from Glasgow. Her husband and health visitor called the doctor in to help:

> *I am still very depressed. My son has colic and cries most of*

the time, and it has affected my husband and other son Mark, as I am always shouting at them for the least thing.

I have now received help from my doctor after a long talk with my husband and my health visitor. I asked my health visitor to call on me as I knew myself I needed some professional help.

Some women needed and received more than just 'someone to talk to'. Where serious postnatal depression developed, the help of a doctor was necessary. **Sheila** is from Croydon:

I was very tearful, easily upset, irritated and annoyed. I took it out mainly on my husband – unable to talk to him until things exploded. I felt as though someone else was controlling my body and my emotions. It was taking me three hours to get to sleep at night, I was so tied up in knots, and then I was awake again from 4.00 a.m. to 5.00 a.m.

At 6½ weeks after the birth my GP prescribed a four-week course of Tryptisol tablets – they helped me to sleep which enabled me to cope with the depression attacks more easily – the attacks became less frequent but when I get them now they last from three to five days (baby is now ten weeks). If I'm still not feeling myself when baby is eleven weeks my GP has asked me to see him again.

Christine, from West Yorkshire, found a short course of tablets helped:

I felt worried, alarmed, totally fed up and as if I'd never smile again. I got a tense tight feeling in the pit of my stomach. I talked to the midwife. She said if I did not get better to see the doctor, which I did. He gave me tablets that made me very sleepy, but my doctor was very understanding. I only took tablets for two days but it cleared up a few days later.

Julia, from Hull, explained how she felt:

Terrible. I felt as if there was no point in living. I did not enjoy the baby at all, I felt a sense of hatred towards him and generally wanted to keep away from everybody else who appeared to love their babies.

After six days in the maternity hospital I went to a mother and baby unit at a mental hospital for a few days to get used to the baby and to be seen by a psychiatrist.

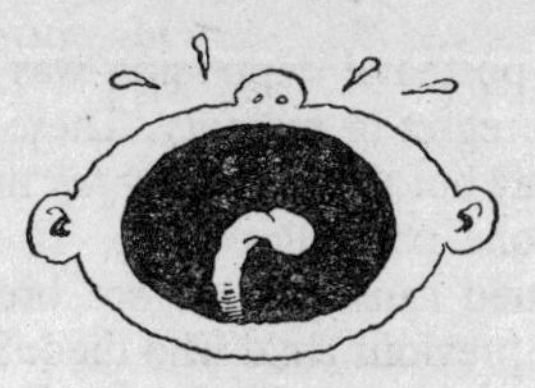

Pamela, from Stockport, found the tablets her GP prescribed made her feel sleepy. She describes her emotions with great clarity and perception. She felt:

. . . panic stricken most of the time, guilt feelings, slightly agrophobic, constant headaches. Very tired, no energy etc. I am possibly too protective of the baby. . . . The health visitor has talked to me a lot but I feel I would rather speak to someone I don't know. The tablets don't help as they only make me sleepy and it doesn't take the feeling away.

Such stories are fortunately very rare. But, by telling us their stories they have helped to draw attention to a problem which until recently was scarcely discussed in public. The more the mothers of tomorrow are aware that new mothers do very occasionally suffer acute mental illness after childbirth, the more ready they will be to go and seek help from their doctor.

Another benefit which results from more open discussion of postnatal depression, both mild and severe, is that women will find their families more understanding. It is sometimes difficult for the sufferer herself to realize what is happening or to seek help if she does. **Lynn**, from Surrey, suffered not only from depression but also from a lack of understanding from her husband. She is a book-keeper:

. . . my husband does not understand the depression I have occasionally suffered from. When the midwife called it postnatal depression he scoffed. It seems that to him and many friends this has a stigma and I, his wife, cannot possibly suffer from it.

Susan, from Derbyshire, is a shorthand writer. She could not even bring herself to ask for help, a feeling common in depression:

I had no help because I didn't tell anyone, even my husband, how awful I felt.

For many women postnatal depression was triggered by some problem or special regret or memory. These women might well have felt low anyway but they certainly *felt* that their depression was triggered by one particular thing. Tiredness is the most commonly mentioned cause but so are breastfeeding worries and memories of a previous child who died. Some women recall times past and regret the lost freedoms of a childless life. This is one reason why second-time mothers seem to feel less depression than first-time mothers. First-time mothers are more likely to yearn for life as it used to be and even to wish that the new baby would just go away, a feeling which is perhaps more common than we care to admit. **Janice**, from Gravesend, is a secretary. She was:

. . . not sure if I was depressed because of birth circumstances and being made to stay in hospital or postnatal depression. I felt desolate and just wanted my husband. I found it unbearable that he was only allowed in twice a day for an hour and visitors came then, I wished the baby would go away so everything could be as it was.

Sheila, from Southampton, said:

I felt very depressed for about six weeks after Mark's birth – unable to cope with him or with anything else. I think my depression was greatly aggravated by problems with feeding and the lack of medical help or care with this.

Elizabeth is from Acton in London:

I felt that everything that had gone wrong with my pregnancy was my fault.

Madeleine, from Hertfordshire, said she felt:

completely depressed owing to the fact that this was my third and last pregnancy and I now have three boys and on each occasion I had hoped for and wanted a girl.

Yvonne is from Watford. She felt:

Terrible. Sometimes I just wanted to cry. I think I feel more depressed this time because my Dad died at the beginning of my pregnancy and I was very close to him and he was devoted to my daughter and longed for a grandson as my brother also had a daughter (we now both have a son since my father's death).

Gillian, from Keighley, is a woolpacker. For many women coming home from hospital improved their morale, breastfeeding seemed easier and getting home to family and friends cheered them up in no time. For others, however, coming home meant less companionship and could even trigger depression:

. . . while in hospital I felt really well and couldn't wait to get home with the baby. But when I was at home I was always crying and didn't want to be left alone. It was a horrible feeling.

Linda is from Gloucestershire:

It's as if there is too much to do and there will never be any time again to do anything I want to do myself.

Julia is from Basingstoke:

I wanted all my free time back – I got fed up with incessant interruptions and wanted to be left alone. I found it intolerable when the baby had to be fed in the night. And I repeatedly used to shout and scream when I had to get up in the night.

Linda, from Humberside, also felt that looking after a baby as well as doing other chores was too much for her:

I used to be a person in my own right. Now all I am is somebody (or something) to feed, wash and change her. In between feeds I am just here to clean the house, wash clothes and feed the rest of the family. I feel unattractive and tired. I am glad I have got her, I just wish that somebody would take the work load off me.

For women who had a previous baby which died, whether at birth, in infancy or childhood, the birth of a new baby can be a particularly painful and poignant time. However much they have come to terms with the tragedy the arrival of another baby can rekindle memories and feelings of guilt or inadequacy. Will this baby be all right? Am I capable of looking after a baby?

. . . and also a deep feeling that another baby cannot ever replace the one that died. **Janice**, from Woking, is a civil servant. Her first daughter died in an accident:

> *. . . my depression is postnatal because I have just had a baby, but really I'm depressed because of the death of my first daughter sixteen months previously. I was depressed during the pregnancy as well.*

Barbara is from Brentwood:

> *The death of my little girl has hit me again, as the new baby boy looks very like she did at birth and in the early weeks. Most of the time I am quite happy but tears release tension.*

The feeling of total despair that comes with the death of a new baby is probably, for most mothers and fathers, beyond words. **Joan**, from Bristol, did describe her feelings and her husband's. The need for family or friends to 'gather round' at such moments is well expressed. Her touching and tragic story also reveals the depth of the feelings of the father as well as the mother:

> *The baby was born with a heart disorder. When the baby was given to me after birth, the nurses left us alone with him. We had to call for the nurse to tell her the baby was a funny colour. She called in a doctor who ordered him to be taken to Special Care Unit. The baby died at 5.30 p.m. Just 2 hours 41 minutes old.*
>
> *He was taken away in the labour room. The nurses brought back my dead baby for me to cuddle. I was still in a ward with other mothers with their healthy babies. I was moved to a side ward later that day.*
>
> *The depression was due to the death of my baby. I felt very guilty because it was a boy and I'd wanted a girl. I only wish now that he had been spared and I had died in his place.*
>
> *No help had been arranged. I had no friends or relatives close at hand. However, following the death of my baby my mother-in-law travelled 200 miles to come and stay for two weeks.*
>
> *Although my husband took no interest in the baby before he was born, he broke his heart for days after the baby's death. He was very helpful and understanding.*

Postnatal depression, four-day blues, or however else the emotional upheavals of the weeks after birth are described, was experienced by most *That's Life* mothers. This fact alone is an encouraging sign of the open and informed approach to postnatal problems which is becoming more common.

Women are now more likely to have heard about the mood swings and possibly more serious mental disorders which can arise after birth and are therefore better able to recognize it and regard it as 'normal'. However, it is a sad fact that we heard from women who told us about their feelings of misery and loneliness or worse but who said they had not been able to talk to anyone else about them. There is much that can be done to alleviate depression or cure more serious disorders. But for a problem to be halved it must be shared.

Home and dry

Bringing a new baby home from hospital is the climax of the nine long months of pregnancy and childbirth. All the preparations: the newly decorated baby room; the sparkling white nappies; the pretty crib are all waiting for the baby to arrive. Bringing a first baby home is a moment of the greatest significance. The couple becomes a family. The home, no longer just a base from which to go out to work, is transformed into a humming, noisy and busy place in which the vital task of raising children will take place.

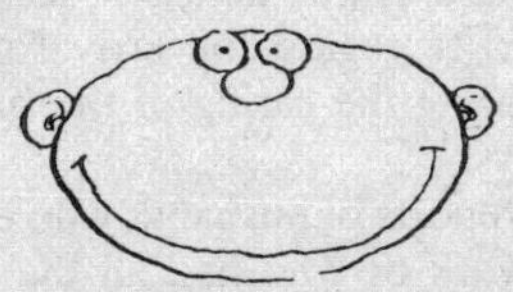

This feeling of elation at coming home is soon replaced for most women by a more realistic mood. As interrupted nights and increased domestic work take their toll, tiredness is experienced by nearly all new mothers, in the early weeks after returning home. Extra help was available in the home to 88 per cent of women – mostly from husbands who now frequently take time off work (either paternity leave, or more commonly annual holiday). Other women had their mother or sisters to help. The

12 per cent of women who had no help on returning home were more likely to feel 'got down' or thoroughly miserable than those who could rest when they felt tired and share the housework and childcare with husband or relative.

Women having their second or subsequent child were especially likely to need practical help, while first-time mothers were more in need of companionship and discussion of feelings and problems. But for most women coming home with a new baby it is to their husbands or partners that they turn both for practical support and for emotional comfort.

A tower of strength?

For a man he's great.

My husband does his best within his limited knowledge of the domestic scene.

I find husbands don't always appreciate how a pregnancy and birth can affect a woman.

I do think that men are more aware today of what women go through in childbirth.

Eighty per cent of women reported their husbands or partners were 'helpful and sympathetic' and 19 per cent 'sometimes helpful and sympathetic'. Only 1 per cent said their husbands were 'not at all helpful and sympathetic'. It seems husbands are on the whole prepared to regard the arrival of a baby as a joint responsibility – sharing the caring of the baby from the beginning, but not always.

There were still reports of husbands who either regarded baby care as woman's work or who had all the right intentions but somehow were 'just too busy'. But by and large it is encouraging to hear of so many couples where the husband ran the house and looked after the older children for a week, or longer, while mother took things easy.

Are husbands becoming more helpful to their wives after the birth of their baby? Certainly there are still men who regard helping as 'cissy' or who have very little knowledge, interest or understanding of what childbirth means to a woman. However, there were many reports of husbands who regard the having and caring for a baby as a completely joint responsibility.

Husbands' and fathers' attitudes to childbirth were not the subject of the survey. However, such an enquiry might reveal some interesting and unexpected findings. How does a husband feel about his spouse changing from wife to mother? Do husbands feel suddenly excluded from a world in which they see no role for themselves? Do they regret the passing of the time when they were perhaps the centre of their wives' world? Does the arrival of a baby alter the nice cosy couple relationship into a family with endless relatives and others forever on the doorstep? Do husbands find it hard to adjust to coming home to a crying baby, no meal and a ratty wife after a long hard day? The answers by fathers to most of these questions would probably be yes.

However, as men and women increasingly share roles at home and at work it is likely that childbirth will become less and less a moment when husband and wives start to go their 'separate ways' (many separating couples report that their marriage started to go wrong after the birth of the first child). Hopefully in the future childbirth will bring couples closer together rather than the reverse. The presence of the husband at the birth is a most significant move in this direction.

These quotes are from women whose husbands were 'towers of strength' in the early weeks and who felt even more loving and close to their husbands as a result. **Brenda** is from Middlesex:

> *My husband (for all his faults) gave me a whole two weeks of complete rest. He was up to the elbows in suds, laundry, cooking, cleaning and ironing, also childminding. It did him good as he works away and now understands more of my job as mother and housewife and appreciates the woman he married.*

Jane, from the Shetland Islands, said:

My husband has been much more understanding than I thought he would be. He has put up with my short temper caused when the baby has been awkward at a feed, or through tiredness. He has helped with the housework and cooking and seen that I get as much rest as possible. He reassures me that I'm doing fine and is really proud of the baby and tries to help all he can with nappies and bath time etc. When I get up at night to feed the baby he gets up and makes me a cuppa.

Denise is from Stanmore:

My husband has been wonderful and has shared all the chores of looking after our daughter. Except nappy changing, but we are working on that.

Carol, from Redhill, also praised her husband:

He does not complain when I moan at him so my frustrations are easily dispersed. Prepared to muck in with chores or to cuddle the restless baby or take over the toddler. My knowledge that he will relieve the pressure at the end of the day/week is vital to my morale. Then it feels like teamwork.

Margaret, a teacher from Newcastle, found she had one problem with her husband:

He helps with rinsing nappies, general cleaning up, he now does all the shopping for food etc. The drawback is it takes me fifteen minutes to wake him up for the night feed!

Jean, from Merseyside, said:

I have been married twice and my first two children are by my ex-husband. My husband now has been very helpful and understanding as he has helped me and my first two children such a lot and has played a large role by attending the birth of our own two children, by cooking, washing and coping with nearly everything.

Janice is from Melksham in Wiltshire. Her comment that '*we* had this baby' was typical of many:

We have always done everything together . . . we had this baby. My husband has taken over many of the household chores including the preparation of meals, washing up, looking after and changing our other child (still in nappies) . . . now I am able to cope as I have a set routine but we still share the duties and I get many days off.

Sharing the care in the early days can set a pattern for the future . . . a father who has cared for his baby from birth is likely to feel more involved in his child than one who has not. **Jane** from Luton suffered from rheumatoid arthritis after her baby was born, but found her husband very helpful:

He will do anything, cooks, looks after our two-year-old, tucks me up in bed and waits on us . . . even though after all his efforts the house may look like a bomb site . . . he tries and cares very much.

Anne pointed out how beneficial the presence of the father can be to older children when a new baby arrives:

My two older girls are very attached to their father and he handles the baby very easily and confidently, so between us we were able to give our attention to all the girls evenly which helped reduce any jealousy and made for a peaceful house and a calm and relaxed atmosphere.

Susan, from Kings Lynn, pointed out how having her husband present at the birth had got them off to the right start:

I thought he would be in the way by wanting to be at the birth but it was the opposite, we have been brought closer together by sharing the experience. He has been a tower of strength through my pregnancy and the birth and since he has helped me look after both children.

Susan, from Wrexham, said:

Nothing is too much trouble for my husband. This is my third child and my husband's first. My first husband was killed in a road traffic accident nine and a half years ago so this child is very much wanted – it's taken seven years to get pregnant.

Many women said their only regret about breastfeeding was that it excluded their husbands, from feeding their babies. **Linda** is from York:

He doesn't object if we don't have our Sunday lunch until

Monday evening. Seriously though, he's helping with housework and shopping and looking after both children. The only thing he can't turn his hand to is breastfeeding.

Lynn is from Bexley Heath:

Sometimes I get a bit ratty if things get fraught with clash of interests due to unveiling of breasts instead of dishing up a meal or such like. (The only disadvantage to breastfeeding being mother's monopoly of breasts!)

Christine, from West Yorkshire, like several mothers, felt that husbands should have paternity leave when a new baby is born and not have to take annual leave:

. . . my husband was extremely helpful. I came home after forty-eight hours and found I was able to rest for as long as I wanted and gradually begin to do some housework, doing a little more each day . . . I feel husbands should be given at least one week (two if possible) paternity leave to give support to their wives, especially when there are older children to look after, instead of having to use their holiday.

Catriona, from Cumbria, is a freelance photographer. Her husband is a marine engineer and fortunately was on leave (not paternity leave) at the time of the baby's birth:

He was always there to mop up tears in the first week at home and was generally a positive tower of strength. I'm very lucky to be married to him and doubly lucky that he'd been at home on leave some two weeks before the birth. I couldn't have got through the birth without him and I can't imagine how I'll cope when he goes back to sea (although I will!).

Some firms and employers do grant paternity leave but they are few and far between. There is no statutory right at present to paid time off for fathers when a baby is born.

Christine is a book-keeper. She felt annoyed with her husband when he failed to take leave as promised:

My husband did say he would have time off when I came home, so I refused the offer of a home help. But he didn't have time off and I was left with the baby and two older children off school for the Easter holidays. Over the past four weeks he has become more helpful and has twice got up in the night to feed the baby.

Derek and **Silkie** from North Shields were one of several couples who took exception to the survey being addressed to the mothers and not the fathers. Should we have addressed the survey to both? We include at length Silkie and Derek's letter because it expresses clearly the feelings of those couples who approach childbirth in a spirit of equality. Unfortunately this approach is less common than they (and we) would like. However, it is hoped that bearing and rearing children will increasingly be seen as a joint responsibility and a joint activity. But there is a long way to go yet. The granting of paternity leave as a statutory right would greatly encourage this process. First **Derek** writes:

Thank you for sending us your survey, which we found very comprehensive. There is one point, however, we were disappointed about: the survey was only addressed to the mother, not to the father as well.

It is a fact of life that it takes two people to produce a child, why exclude the father in the care of it?

We find it annoying when adverts for childcare products only appeal to the mother, worse when in medical programmes about children's health, etc. reference is only made to the worries a mother might have, rarely to the worries a father might have. Only two examples:

1. When recently the issue of an insurance against handicapped children was discussed in the media, it was the worries of the mother of the unborn child that were discussed. The worries of the father of that same unborn child were not mentioned. Am I the only father in England who is concerned that my child might be handicapped?

2. In a recent radio programme about cot death, reference was made only to the worries of mother, to the care and vigilance of mother. What about the father? Is he not worried? Does he not watch over his child? Does he not give up much needed sleep by having the baby cot in the parental bedroom so that baby can be heard if he is in trouble?

And **Silkie** writes:

> *I, as a mother, find the role of the father of our child most important, during pregnancy as well as afterwards.*
>
> *Our marriage or our baby would be under severe stress if I had to divide my loyalty and love between my husband and 'my' child, instead of us two together loving and caring for him.*
>
> *It is a matter of our convenience that my husband goes out to earn the money and I look after household and child. But this does not mean that our baby would be as healthy as it is without the support of his father.*
>
> *If my husband did not care about our child, I would have had a rotten time during pregnancy, because he might not be willing to put up with my tiredness and bad moods. If he had not cared for our unborn child, he would not have supported me in suffering pains during pregnancy rather than taking painkillers which might have damaged the child (that meant a bad-tempered wife for him). He might not give me a helping hand when I am worn out through breastfeeding. He would just say, 'Put him on the bottle, then you will be less exhausted and more fun for me'. Surely the husband is a major factor in the well-being of the baby, a healthy pregnancy, a healthy birth and a healthy child.*

The quotes that follow are from women who commented on their husband's reactions to the birth of a new baby. Some did not find their husbands as helpful as they would have wished. **Jean** is from Rotherham:

> *I find husbands don't always appreciate how a pregnancy and birth can affect a woman. Because I had a quick labour/delivery he thinks that I should feel marvellously well, he doesn't realize it affects you emotionally after carrying something inside you for nine months and suddenly it's all over and you have to readjust your life.*

Margaret is from Ormskirk:

> *For a man he's great. But I think no man can ever really understand just what a woman feels and experiences at this time.*

Julie is from Hull:

He didn't understand about depression being an illness and can't offer much sympathy when I have a day when things get on top of me. He loses his temper when I suddenly burst into tears and that makes me much worse.

Amanda from Hampstead spoke for many women when she said:

He does intend to be helpful and says things like 'Don't do the washing-up, I'll do it' but two hours later it's still sitting there – so I do it and then he gets angry with me.

Alison is from Bristol:

I felt that if I told anybody how I felt they would think I was stupid. I think this is because my husband thinks I am grumbling about nothing.

Jean is from Stroud:

Like most men they feel we can cope with all the extra work plus disturbed nights also keeping the rest of the family happy, not realizing how tired we get and offering that bit of extra help. Mine still likes his cup of tea in bed before getting up, so do I, but not a chance!

Vanessa, from Shawbury in Shropshire, wrote:

He is very helpful with the baby – he baths and changes her quite often. He just tends to forget that I have to live in a very restricting routine and wonders why I have achieved so little in the day in the way of housework and gardening etc.

Alison, from Bristol, again:

I feel very isolated. I live in a strange area and I don't know anybody. I feel every day is the same, my husband never takes me out, and he does not understand how I feel, he just tells me 'how do you think other women manage? You're not the only one.' That comment doesn't do much for my morale.

Patricia is from South Yorkshire. Many women said their husbands expected them to cope normally after getting home from hospital:

He didn't realize how tired I felt until I came home. When sitting in bed in hospital, they don't see you walking around like a decrepit snail because of stitches. I think he expects me to come home and continue rushing about, doing everything as before.

June, from Bristol, is a nursery nurse:

He feels that his job is from 8.30 a.m. to 5.00 p.m. and is very tiring – mine is apparently twenty-four hours a day and seven days a week. He doesn't feel obliged to help in the work of caring for the children.

Rosemary, from Fareham, did not appreciate her husband's response to her return from hospital:

When I came home (the same morning) he took the floorboards up in the kitchen and started to tile the floor. He thought I would be back to get him proper meals. He expected I would turn into a well organized mum overnight. He just didn't understand that I wasn't up to it all straight away. I didn't get the help needed until I went to my mother a week later.

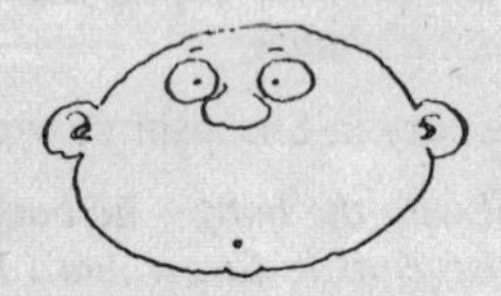

Lynda from Redcar is a nurse:

He was very helpful and did most things around the house – cooking, washing up etc., at first, but now he can't seem to understand why his dinner isn't ready on time and comes out with things like, 'You say you're tired, you haven't done anything all day. I've been to work, remember.' He doesn't seem to realize I'm tired and it's a full-time job looking after Christopher.

Eileen, from Cornwall, expressed particularly strong feelings:

I feel very angry with all men and very resentful of their easy pain-free lives . . . women certainly seem to get a raw deal in life. I have very little patience with my partner in particular and men in general. I feel I would get on better without my partner . . . he just makes extra work for me and while not actively disliking the baby cannot be bothered with him either.

Some of the women in our survey were unmarried, separated or divorced (3 per cent). These women were especially likely to feel anxious and lonely once home from hospital. Those women who had only recently been separated from a partner or husband were particularly vulnerable.

Other women had serious housing or financial problems which greatly aggravated the difficulties of settling in with a new baby. **Maree**, from Surrey, experienced many of the problems associated with being a single mother:

I am divorced and have one child by that marriage. In April 1980 I went and lived with a man and we decided to let Nature take its course. However, when I fell pregnant it was a big contributing factor to our relationship breakdown. I moved out in November 1980 to live with my five-year-old son and widowed mother. I have had no support whatsoever from the man and have been through tremendous pressure regarding my own financial matters before the birth. Now, I have the trouble of obtaining maintenance for the baby as I am unable to work full time.

Christine, from Bradford, had a very stressful pregnancy. She is not married and was unemployed. Her baby weighed only 5lb 3oz although it was two weeks overdue. Stress during pregnancy can have an effect on the baby's growth:

My boyfriend left me when I refused to have an abortion. I saw him two months before I had the baby but since I've had the baby I've heard nothing . . . he has not even bothered to ask how I am.

Christine, from Muswell Hill, is unmarried and has an older child who is spastic:

Because my little boy is handicapped, I was worried how I was going to cope on my own as the children's father had left us . . . I found my family were very understanding and helped me very much.

Sandra is from Barking. Unsuitable housing created real difficulties for her with two young children. She felt:

trapped, owing to accommodation – very cold and damp. And I am unable to get out much due to stairs, as we live on the eleventh floor and the lift only goes to the tenth floor. Very awkward with pram and children.

Have spoken to health visitors at clinic but they cannot do anything owing to rent arrears.

Women with new babies can feel fragile and vulnerable. Even the most happily married couple with a much wanted baby and no housing or financial difficulties will experience moments of stress and exhaustion in the weeks after a new baby arrives. It would be strange if such a momentous event as having a baby could occur without affecting the temporary stability of the mother. However, with plenty of love, support and practical help, depression or weepiness soon passes. For those women where support and love is not to hand the postnatal period can be more difficult.

All new mothers, whoever they are, need to be cared for so they, in their turn, can give their babies the best possible start in life. It seems clear from our survey that the husband and father is the most effective provider of this care. By being closely involved in the care of his wife and baby in the early weeks a pattern is set for the future family . . . a pattern where 'care is shared' and where demarcation lines between 'women's work' and 'men's work' are few. There are no losers in such a pattern, mother, father, and above all children, all win.

5 What 6,000 Women Told Us

All women who were sent a questionnaire also received a letter explaining why and how the survey was being conducted. The letter emphasized that what we wanted was not only simple Yes/ No answers to straightforward questions and ringing of multiple choice answers, but also, to give women a unique chance to express their personal feelings, deeper reactions and thoughts about pregnancy and childbirth. As we have said before, these subjective impressions, which were such an important part of the survey cannot be 'computerized'. They are rather an elaboration of the statistics – the real stories behind the figures.

This chapter is concerned purely to record the statistical results of the survey – a little balder, perhaps, but no less fascinating.

Your details

Where you live? (defined according to Regional Health Authorities)

Sample: 5883

	*Number**	*Percentage**
1 Scotland	323	5
2 Northern Ireland	32	1
3 Northern	233	4
4 Yorkshire	336	6
5 North Western	292	5
6 Merseyside	260	4

	Number*	Percentage*
7 Trent	481	8
8 Wales	188	3
9 West Midlands	417	7
10 East Anglia	198	3
11 Oxford	390	7
12 North West Thames	331	6
13 North East Thames	381	6
14 South East Thames	439	7
15 South West Thames	412	7
16 Wessex	368	6
17 South Western	438	7
18 Forces	27	0
19 A London Hospital	331	6

* Whenever the numbers do not add up to the total sample, or the percentages do not add up to 100, this is because some answers on the questions were either unclear or 'spoilt'.

Age *Sample:* 5832

	Number	Percentage
up to 16	7	0
17–20	196	3
21–25	1908	33
26–30	2480	43
31–35	1061	18
36–40	170	3
41 and over	10	0

Average: 27
Oldest: 44

Husband/partner's occupation *Sample:* 5794

	Number	Percentage
1 Professional	564	10
2 Intermediate	1529	26
3 Skilled non-manual	1068	18
4 Skilled manual	1621	28
5 Semi-skilled	611	11
6 Unskilled	90	2
7 Unemployed	265	5

Are you married? *Sample:* 5914

	Number	*Percentage*
Yes	5578	94
No	277	4

SECTION 1 – WHILE YOU ARE PREGNANT

General

1 When is your baby due? *Sample:* 5826

	*Number**	*Percentage*
January 1981	40	1
February	261	4
March	647	11
April	789	14
May	883	15
June	863	15
July	1084	19
August	859	15
September	239	4
October	101	2
November	39	1
December	16	0

* Most babies were expected at the beginning or the middle of the year due to the timing of the survey.

2 How many weeks pregnant were you when your pregnancy was confirmed? *Sample:* 5795

	Number	*Percentage*
up to 4 weeks	283	5
5–8 weeks	3840	66
9–12 weeks	1423	25
13–16 weeks	189	3
17 weeks and over	60	1

Average: 8 weeks

3 Have you had any babies before? *Sample:* 5879

	Number	*Percentage*
Yes	3630	62
No	2230	38

If so how many? *Sample:* 3630

0	88	2*
1	2463	68
2	819	23
3	191	5
4	42	1
5	15	0
6	8	0

* Of course, there should be no numbers here and we can only assume that some women answered Yes to the first part of question 3, and then failed to answer the second part for the number of children.

Were they all born healthy? *Sample:* 3630

Yes	3208	88
No	352	10

4 Have you ever had a miscarriage? *Sample:* 5866

	Number	*Percentage*
Yes	1098	19
No	4745	81

How many miscarriages have you had? *Sample:* 1098

1	862	79
2	181	16
3	39	4
4	9	1
5	3	0
6	2	0

5 Have you ever had a pregnancy terminated (abortion)?
(This question was optional) *Sample:* 5709

	Number	*Percentage*
Yes	371	6
No	5334	93

6 Were you ever advised to go to an antenatal clinic (GP or hospital clinic)? *Sample:* 5732

	Number	*Percentage*
Yes	5161	90
No	518	9

If so, who *first* advised you to go? *Sample:* 5161

a) your GP	3864	75
b) a midwife	127	2
c) a friend or relative	65	1
d) your own initiative	1072	21

7 Were you visited at home by a midwife during your pregnancy? *Sample:* 5804

	Number	*Percentage*
a) never	2823	49
b) once or twice	2603	45
c) regularly	364	6

8 How was your antenatal care organized? *Sample:* 5886

	Number	*Percentage*
a) by your GP	1197*	20*
b) by a hospital	571	10
c) by both the above	3961	67
d) local authority clinic	108	2
e) private clinic	31	1
f) no antenatal care	8	0

* These figures are undoubtedly a little higher than they should be because some women assumed that their GPs 'organized' their antenatal care as he or she was the first person to make the arrangements for their antenatal care, even though the care may subsequently have been shared with the hospital.

Hospital clinic (only for those who attended a hospital clinic)

10 How many miles was your hospital clinic from your home?

Sample: 4849

	Number	*Percentage*
up to 1 mile	652	13
over 1 and up to 2 miles	707	15
over 2 and up to 3 miles	714	15
over 3 and up to 4 miles	502	10
over 4 and up to 5 miles	496	10
over 5 and up to 10 miles	1071	22
over 10 and up to 15 miles	405	8
over 15 miles	302	6

Average: 6 miles
Longest journey: 64 miles

11 How did you usually get to your hospital clinic?

Sample: 5101

	Number	*Percentage*
a) public transport	1502	29
b) car	3057	60
c) walk	469	9
d) other	68	1

12 How long did it take you to get to your hospital clinic?

Sample: 5082

	Number	*Percentage*
a) up to half-an-hour	3693	73
b) half-an-hour to an hour	1184	23
c) more than an hour	204	4

13 How much did it cost to get to your hospital clinic?

Sample: 4648

	Number	*Percentage*
a) up to 50p	2392	51
b) 50p to £1	1475	32
c) more than £1	765	16

14 On average, how long did you have to wait per visit?

Sample: 5069

	Number	Percentage
a) up to half-an-hour	1078	21
b) half-an-hour to an hour	1645	32
c) one to two hours	1880	37
d) more than two hours	454	9

15 Was your hospital clinic open after 6 p.m.? *Sample:* 4650*

	Number	Percentage
Yes	163	4
No	4478	96

* Some women did not answer this question probably because they did not know the answer.

16 Were there facilities for young children at your hospital clinic (e.g. toys, crèche)? *Sample:* 4968

	Number	Percentage
Yes	2310	46
No	2657	53

17 Were there any refreshments available at your hospital clinic? *Sample:* 5052

	Number	Percentage
Yes	3252	64
No	1790	35

Your antenatal visits

18 How many weeks pregnant were you when you had your first antenatal check-up (GP or hospital clinic)?

Sample: 5861

	Number	Percentage
up to 12 weeks	4564	78
13–16 weeks	1048	18
17–20 weeks	186	3
21–24 weeks	33	1
25 weeks and over	30	1

Average: 11 weeks

19 How often did you visit an antenatal clinic (GP or hospital)?* *Sample:* 5694

a) in the first 28 weeks	*Number*	*Percentage*
once	96	2
twice	153	3
3 times	430	8
4 times	1929	34
5 times	1561	27
6 times	706	12
7 times	409	7
8 times	208	4
9 times	202	4

Average: 5 times

b) 29th to 36th week *Sample:* 5461

once	75	1
twice	386	7
3 times	1040	19
4 times	2958	54
5 times	448	8
6 times	84	5
7 times	48	2
8 times	66	2
9 times	30	1

Average: 4 times

c) 37th week to delivery *Sample:* 4982

	Number	*Percentage*
once	215	4
twice	349	7
3 times	1245	25
4 times	2692	54

* Question 19 was phrased in a slightly misleading way so that many women answered, e.g. a) 'every 4 weeks', b) 'every 2 weeks' and c) 'every week'. We therefore had to estimate the number of times these women actually went to the clinic in the given period. Hence, the average probably is the best guide.

The sample for c) is smaller because we assume a number of women were either in hospital for the latter few weeks of pregnancy or they might have had a premature birth.

	Number	Percentage
5 times	287	6
6 times	111	2
7 times	37	1
8 times	30	1
9 times	16	0

Average: 4 times

20 If you ever missed antenatal appointments, was it usually because . . . ? *Sample:* 1220

	Number	Percentage
a) of illness	558	46
b) you couldn't afford the time	62	5
c) you disliked going to the clinic	87	7
d) you felt it was not very important to go	17	1
e) cost of transport	21	2
f) other reason	388	32

21 Did you feel you could ask your hospital doctor questions? *Sample:* 5696

	Number	Percentage
a) freely	2922	51
b) to some extent	2041	36
c) hardly at all	732	13

22 Were your questions answered to your satisfaction? *Sample:* 5711

	Number	Percentage
a) always	2732	48
b) sometimes	2726	48
c) never	251	4

23 Did your antenatal visits make you feel . . . ? *Sample:* 5796

	Number	Percentage
a) important and reassured	2290	40
b) a little reassured	2209	38
c) unimportant	982	17
d) anxious	301	5

24 At your first antenatal check-up, did the examination include . . . ?

a) height	*Number*	*Percentage*
		Sample: 5871
Yes	4676	80
No	1185	20

b) weight		*Sample:* 5903
Yes	5830	99
No	71	1

c) urine test		*Sample:* 5900
Yes	5799	98
No	98	2

d) blood pressure		*Sample:* 5904
Yes	5864	99
No	39	1

e) breast examination		*Sample:* 5862
Yes	3459	59
No	2401	41

f) chest examination (with stethoscope)		*Sample:* 5839
Yes	3584	61
No	2254	39

g) abdomen (tummy) examination		*Sample:* 5891
Yes	5608	95
No	282	5

h) legs and ankles		*Sample:* 5867
Yes	4364	74
No	1501	26

i) internal examination		*Sample:* 5866
Yes	3369	57
No	2492	42

25 On any subsequent visit to the clinic, were the following details ever taken? *Sample:* 5887

a) weight	*Number*	*Percentage*
Yes	5817	99
No	70	1

b) urine test		*Sample:* 5891
Yes	5878	100
No	13	0

c) blood pressure		*Sample:* 5892
Yes	5872	100
No	20	0

d) abdomen (tummy) examination		*Sample:* 5886
Yes	5852	99
No	34	1

e) internal examination		*Sample:* 5745
Yes	2409	42
No	3333	58

26 Was a blood sample ever taken? *Sample:* 5898

	Number	*Percentage*
Yes	5852	99
No	45	1

27 Did you have a blood test for spina bifida?* *Sample:* 5417

	Number	*Percentage*
Yes	2562	47
No	2853	53

* Not everybody answered this question or they wrote in 'don't know'. Many more women may have had this blood test but were unaware that it may have been specifically for spina bifida.

28 Did you have an ultrasound scan? *Sample:* 5873

	Number	*Percentage*
Yes	3773	64
No	2098	36

29 Did you have an amniocentesis test (fluid taken from sac around baby)?* *Sample:* 5914

	Number	*Percentage*
Yes	59	1
No	5855	99

* This test is only significant in very few cases, for example, if the woman is over a certain age or if doctors have some reason to believe that there might be something wrong with the baby.

If so, did the results show signs of any defects? *Sample:* 59

	Number	*Percentage*
Yes	49	63
No	10	17

30 Was the baby's heartbeat ever listened to? *Sample:* 5875

	Number	*Percentage*
Yes	5809	99
No	66	1

If so, did you listen to it? *Sample:* 5809

Yes	2987	51
No	2659	46

31 Were you encouraged to breastfeed?* *Sample:* 5760

	Number	*Percentage*
Yes	4497	78
No	1203	21

If so, who was the *most* encouraging? *Sample:* 4497

a) a doctor	710	16
b) midwife	2014	45
c) your mother	292	6
d) friend or relative	452	10
e) books or leaflets	707	16

32 Were you put off the idea of breastfeeding?* *Sample:* 5914

	Number	*Percentage*
Yes	729	12
No	5185	88

* Questions 31 and 32 referred only to breastfeeding advice during the antenatal period. Other questions about breastfeeding come in the postnatal section. This may have been misleading for some women.

If so, who was the *most* responsible for your decision?

Sample: 729

a) doctor	22	3
b) midwife	34	5
c) your mother	43	6
d) friend or relative	100	14
e) other	514	71

33 At the antenatal clinic, were you given advice on . . . ?

Sample: 5769

a) diet	*Number*	*Percentage*
Yes	3285	57
No	2484	43

b) holidays planned *Sample:* 5684

Yes	693	12
No	4991	88

c) travelling (on any form of transport) *Sample:* 5693

Yes	822	14
No	4870	86

d) rest *Sample:* 5787

Yes	4105	71
No	1682	29

e) exercise *Sample:* 5737

Yes	2753	48
No	2983	52

f) work *Sample:* 5684

	Number	*Percentage*
Yes	1696	30
No	3988	70

g) teeth *Sample:* 5740

Yes	3004	52
No	2736	48

h) free dental treatment *Sample:* 5775

Yes	3514	61
No	2261	39

i) free prescriptions *Sample:* 5778

Yes	4136	72
No	1641	28

34 At the antenatal clinic, were you warned about . . . ?

Sample: 5794

a) smoking

	Number	*Percentage*
Yes	3527	61
No	2267	39

b) alcohol *Sample:* 5763

Yes	2216	38
No	3547	62

c) contact with anyone with German measles *Sample:* 5767

Yes	2591	45
No	3176	55

d) taking drugs (pills, medicines, etc.) *Sample:* 5777

Yes	3001	52
No	2776	48

e) x-rays *Sample:* 5755

Yes	1384	24
No	4368	76

35 Who or what was the *best* source of information about your pregnancy? *Sample:* 5837

		Number	*Percentage*
a)	hospital doctor	803	14
b)	your own GP	1689	29
c)	midwife	913	16
d)	your mother	191	3
e)	friend or relative	348	6
f)	books or leaflets	1058	18
g)	past experience	821	14

36 During your pregnancy, was the hospital doctor . . . ? *Sample:* 5286

		Number	*Percentage*
a)	helpful and sympathetic	2286	43
b)	sometimes helpful and sympathetic	1962	37
c)	not very helpful and sympathetic	1004	19

37 During your pregnancy, was your GP . . . ? *Sample:* 5614

		Number	*Percentage*
a)	helpful and sympathetic	3894	69
b)	sometimes helpful and sympathetic	1223	22
c)	not very helpful and sympathetic	491	9

38 During your pregnancy, was your community midwife . . . ? *Sample:* 4456

		Number	*Percentage*
a)	helpful and sympathetic	3258	73
b)	sometimes helpful and sympathetic	729	16
c)	not very helpful and sympathetic	460	10

39 During your pregnancy, was your hospital midwife . . . ?

Sample: 4205

	Number	*Percentage*
a) helpful and sympathetic	2579	61
b) sometimes helpful and sympathetic	1118	27
c) not very helpful and sympathetic	501	12

Antenatal classes (only for those who attended classes)

40 How did you first hear about the classes?

Sample: 3429

	Number	*Percentage*
a) doctor	879	26
b) midwife	1423	41
c) friend or relative	380	11
d) books or leaflets	123	4
e) found out on your own initiative	607	18

41 How many weeks pregnant were you when you attended your first class?

Sample: 3373

	Number	*Percentage*
up to 24 weeks	583	17
25–28 weeks	793	24
29–32 weeks	1476	44
33–36 weeks	478	14
37 weeks and over	43	1

Average: 28 weeks

42 How were the classes organized?

Sample: 3436

	Number	*Percentage*
a) by the hospital	1297	38
b) by the local GP clinic	1531	45
c) by the National Childbirth Trust	345	10
d) other	251	7

43 What were the subjects covered in the classes?

Sample: 3426

a) relaxation	*Number*	*Percentage*
Yes	3410	100
No	16	0

Sample: 3281

b) parentcraft	*Number*	*Percentage*
Yes	3013	92
No	268	8

Sample: 2544

c) other	*Number*	*Percentage*
Yes	1899	75
No	642	25

44 Were husbands/partners encouraged to take part?

Sample: 3369

	Number	*Percentage*
Yes	2311	69
No	1022	30

45 Were the classes . . . ?

Sample: 3375

	Number	*Percentage*
a) very helpful	1929	57
b) quite helpful	1232	37
c) hardly helpful	200	6

Work (only for those who worked during pregnancy)

46 How many weeks pregnant were you when you stopped work?

Sample: 2688

	Number	*Percentage*
up to 12 weeks	153	6
13–16 weeks	79	3
17–20 weeks	96	4
21–24 weeks	115	4
25–28 weeks	600	22
29–32 weeks	1209	45

	Number	Percentage
33–36 weeks	314	12
37–40 weeks	119	4

Average: 28 weeks

47 Have you claimed for any of these benefits?

Sample: 2960

a) maternity grant	*Number*	*Percentage*
Yes	2893	98
No	56	2

b) maternity allowance/pay *Sample:* 2808

Yes	2456	87
No	347	12

c) maternity leave *Sample:* 2571

Yes	1055	41
No	1511	59

48 If you knew about any of these benefits, how did you *first* find out?

Sample: 2909

	Number	*Percentage*
a) your union	45	2
b) doctor	170	6
c) midwife	181	6
d) friend or relative	419	14
e) books or leaflets	618	21
f) past experience or general knowledge	1463	50

49 Were you given time off, with pay, for your antenatal check-ups?

Sample: 2510

	Number	*Percentage*
Yes	2053	82
No	449	18

50 If you answered 'yes' to the above, was permission given . . . ? *Sample:* 2057

	Number	*Percentage*
a) willingly	1792	87
b) with some reluctance	214	10
c) unwillingly	41	2

51 Was the attitude of your employer towards your pregnancy . . . ? *Sample:* 2595

	Number	*Percentage*
a) understanding	1978	76
b) sometimes understanding	401	15
c) not very understanding	207	8

52 Do you intend to return to work after the birth of your baby? *Sample:* 2777

	Number	*Percentage*
Yes	911	33
No	1857	67

If so, how many months after the birth? *Sample:* 911

under 1 month	135	15
1 month	50	5
2 months	116	13
3 months	147	16
4 months	58	6
5 months	49	5
6 months	215	24
7 months	49	5
8 months	13	1
9 months	12	1
10 months	7	1
11 months	1	0
12 months	29	3
18 months	5	1
24 months	5	1
30 months	2	0
36 months	3	0

Average: 5 months

53 If you are intending to return to work, are the reasons mainly . . . ? *Sample:* 1046

	Number	*Percentage*
a) financial	313	30
b) personal satisfaction	120	11
c) both a) and b)	513	49
d) other	29	3

54 Does your place of work have a crèche? *Sample:* 2012

	Number	*Percentage*
Yes	102	5
No	1988	95

Your health

55 Did you smoke during your pregnancy? *Sample:* 5863

	Number	*Percentage*
a) never	4298	73
b) occasionally	546	9
c) up to 10 a day	370	6
d) more than 10 a day	615	10

56 Did you have any symptoms which made you feel unwell at any time during your pregnancy? *Sample:* 5883

	Number	*Percentage*
Yes	5719	97
No	164	3

If so, did these include . . . ? *Sample:* 5719*

a) sickness

Yes	2960	52
No	2377	42

b) nausea *Sample:* 5719

Yes	3987	70
No	1431	25

* Most of the percentages in questions 56 a) to h) do not add up to 100. This is because some women answered 'Yes' to the first question but then did not answer 'Yes' or 'No' to the specific questions on symptoms.

c) tiredness

	Number	Percentage
		Sample: 5719
Yes	4983	87
No	553	10

d) insomnia

		Sample: 5719
Yes	2462	43
No	2761	48

e) heartburn

		Sample: 5719
Yes	3830	67
No	1609	28

f) constipation

		Sample: 5719
Yes	2402	42
No	2880	50

g) fainting

		Sample: 5719
Yes	955	17
No	4197	73

h) backache

		Sample: 5719
Yes	3788	66
No	1628	28

57 If you had any ailments at all during your pregnancy, did you take *any* pills or medicines (including aspirin etc.) for them?

	Number	Percentage
		Sample: 5823
Yes	4118	71
No	1674	29

If you took any kind of drug, was this . . . ?

		Sample: 4118
a) on your doctor's advice	3279	80
b) on your midwife's advice	90	2
c) on a friend or relative's advice	30	1
d) on your own initiative	588	14

58 Did you have any particular food 'fads' during your pregnancy? *Sample:* 5808

	Number	*Percentage*
Yes	2827	49
No	2976	51

59 Were you told any 'old wives' tales' about pregnancy? *Sample:* 5698

	Number	*Percentage*
Yes	2240	39
No	3442	60

60 During your pregnancy, was your husband/partner . . . ? *Sample:* 5853

	Number	*Percentage*
a) helpful and sympathetic	4196	72
b) sometimes helpful and sympathetic	1459	25
c) not very helpful and sympathetic	182	3

61 Who did you find the *best* person to talk to about your pregnancy? *Sample:* 5807

	Number	*Percentage*
a) doctor	923	16
b) midwife	599	10
c) husband/partner	3161	54
d) your mother	339	6
e) other friend or relative	774	13

62 In general, did you enjoy your pregnancy? *Sample:* 5634

	Number	*Percentage*
Yes	3933	70
No	1673	30

SECTION 2 – HAVING YOUR BABY

General

63 What did your baby weigh? *Sample:* 5879

	Number	*Percentage*
a) less than 2,500 grams (5lb 8oz)	290	5
b) 2,500 grams (5lb 8oz) or more	5582	95

64 Where was your baby born? *Sample:* 5868

	Number	*Percentage*
a) in hospital (with hospital doctor/midwife)	5293	90
b) in hospital (with you own GP looking after you)	388	7
c) at home	119	2
d) other	66	1

Labour

67 How many hours was labour (regular contractions)?
Sample: 5572

	Number	*Percentage*
a) up to 12 hours	4512	81
b) 12–24 hours	883	16
c) more than 24 hours	169	3

68 Was labour induced/started artificially? *Sample:* 5510

	Number	*Percentage*
Yes	1851	34
No	3632	66

If so, was it . . . ? *Sample:* 1851

a) your own wish	184	10
b) on medical grounds	1437	78
c) for convenience of the doctor/ hospital	82	4
d) don't know	88	5

69 Were you left alone during labour . . . ? *Sample:* 5495

	Number	*Percentage*
a) hardly at all	4121	75
b) some of the time	1018	19
c) most of the time	333	6

70 If someone was with you during labour, did it include . . . ? *Sample:* 5425

a) your husband/partner	*Number*	*Percentage*
Yes	4972	92
No	448	8

b) friend or relative		*Sample:* 3837
Yes	248	6
No	3585	93

c) doctor		*Sample:* 4186
Yes	1779	42
No	2404	57

d) midwife		*Sample:* 5089
Yes	4657	92
No	429	8

e) nurse		*Sample:* 4607
Yes	3264	71
No	1343	29

f) other		*Sample:* 3774
Yes	630	17
No	3135	83

71 Did you enjoy labour . . . ? *Sample:* 5537

	Number	*Percentage*
a) most of the time	1615	29
b) some of the time	2038	37
c) not at all	1870	34

Delivery

72 What kind of delivery did you have? *Sample:* 5873

	Number	*Percentage*
a) normal	4488	76
b) forceps	764	13
c) vacuum extraction	45	1
d) Caesarian	565	10
e) don't know	7	0

74 Did you have . . . ? *Sample:* 4359

	Number	*Percentage*
a) an episiotomy (cut) which was then stitched	2712	62
b) a spontaneous tear which was then stitched	1287	30
c) both the above	324	7

75 Was the baby's heart monitored at any time during delivery? *Sample:* 5726

	Number	*Percentage*
Yes	5190	91
No	479	8

If so, by what method?* *Sample:* 5190

a) trumpet	1865	36
b) belt monitor (around mother's abdomen/tummy)	1290	25
c) scalp monitor (on baby's head)	1863	36
d) don't know	105	2

* This question was phrased in such a way that it did not allow for more than one answer to be recorded on the computer. However, many women ringed b) and c). When this happened, we recorded c) as this was the method requiring a greater degree of medical intervention.

76 Did you have any painkillers during labour and/or delivery? *Sample:* 5914

	Number	*Percentage*
Yes	5029	85
No	885	15

If so, were you given . . . ?*

Sample: 5029

	Number	*Percentage*
a) pethidine	2513	50
b) epidural (spinal injection)	800	16
c) gas and oxygen	1347	27
d) general anaesthetic	314	6
e) other	47	1

* Again, this question did not permit more than one answer to be recorded, although many women had ringed, for example, a) and c) because they had both pethidine and gas and oxygen. Hence, the figure for gas and oxygen and pethidine should be higher as we always recorded the drug which had a greater degree of medical interference when more than one answer was ringed. A general anaesthetic was recorded in preference to an epidural, an epidural to pethidine and pethidine to gas and oxygen.

77 If you had any kind of painkiller, was it discussed with you beforehand?

Sample: 5029

	Number	*Percentage*
Yes	3689	73
No	1153	23

78 If you had any kind of painkiller, was it . . . ?

Sample: 5029

	Number	*Percentage*
a) offered to you	3627	72
b) requested by you	1102	22

79 If you had any kind of painkiller, was it . . . ?

Sample: 5029

	Number	*Percentage*
a) very effective	2226	44
b) slightly effective	2115	42
c) not at all effective	496	10

80 Did you have any friend or relative with you during delivery?

Sample: 5725

	Number	*Percentage*
Yes	3515	61
No	2196	38

If not, was it mainly . . . ? *Sample:* 2196

	Number	*Percentage*
a) your own wish	1035	47
b) on medical grounds	301	14
c) the doctor's/midwife's wish	88	4
d) hospital routine	139	6
e) other	378	17

81 Was there a doctor present at delivery . . . ? *Sample:* 5754

	Number	*Percentage*
a) all the time	1532	27
b) some of the time	1035	18
c) not at all	3052	53
d) don't know	109	2

82 If there was a doctor present at delivery, had you met him/her before? *Sample:* 2847

	Number	*Percentage*
Yes	1491	52
No	1347	47

83 If there was a midwife present at delivery had you met her before? *Sample:* 5583

	Number	*Percentage*
Yes	1516	27
No	4064	73

84 Were there any serious problems for the baby during labour/delivery? *Sample:* 5625

	Number	*Percentage*
Yes	1187	21
No	4430	79

85 Were there any serious problems for you during labour/delivery? *Sample:* 5652

	Number	*Percentage*
Yes	778	14
No	4866	86

86 Were you told what was happening during delivery . . . ?

Sample: 5529

	Number	*Percentage*
a) most of the time	4021	73
b) some of the time	875	16
c) hardly at all	625	11

87 Did you feel the medical people around you were . . . ?

Sample: 5782

	Number	*Percentage*
a) mostly helpful and sympathetic	4976	86
b) sometimes helpful and sympathetic	646	11
c) not at all helpful and sympathetic	152	3

88 Did you feel you had reasonable freedom of choice about . . . ?

a) position during labour (e.g. walking, sitting) *Sample:* 5445

	Number	*Percentage*
Yes	3234	59
No	2209	41

b) use of painkillers *Sample:* 5438

Yes	4504	83
No	933	17

c) position in which you gave birth *Sample:* 5400

Yes	2297	43
No	3101	57

d) when the baby was given to you after delivery

Sample: 5469

Yes	4349	80
No	1118	20

89 After delivery, was your baby given to you to hold

Sample: 5732

	Number	*Percentage*
a) immediately	4330	76
b) within an hour	1096	19
c) within days	291	5

90 Did you enjoy the birth of your baby? *Sample:* 5442

	Number	*Percentage*
Yes	3938	72
No	1483	27

91 During your pregnancy and childbirth, would you have preferred . . . ? *Sample:* 5850

	Number	*Percentage*
a) a male doctor	476	8
b) a female doctor	663	11
c) no preference	4707	80

SECTION 3 – AFTER HAVING YOUR BABY

Baby's details

Weight *Sample:* 5831

	Number	*Percentage*
up to 1 kg (2lb 3oz)	13	0
over 1 kg and up to 1.5 kg (2lb 3oz–3lb 5oz)	30	1
over 1.5 kg and up to 2 kg (3lb 5oz–4lb 7oz)	49	1
over 2 kg and up to 2.5 kg (4lb 7oz–5lb 8oz)	176	3
over 2.5 kg and up to 3 kg (5lb 8oz–6lb 10oz)	823	14
over 3 kg and up to 3.5 kg (6lb 10oz–7lb 11oz)	2278	39
over 3.5 kg and up to 4 kg (7lb 11oz–8lb 13oz)	1878	32
over 4 kg and up to 4.5 kg (8lb 13oz–9lb 14oz)	494	8
over 4.5 kg and up to 5 kg (9lb 14oz–11lb)	71	1
over 5 kg (over 11lb)	19	0

Average: 3.40 kg (7lb 8oz)
Heaviest baby: 5.78 kg (12lb 12oz)

Sex of baby *Sample:* 5851

	Number	Percentage
Boy	2993	51
Girl	2815	48

Date of birth *Sample:* 5862

January	21	0
February	314	5
March	664	11
April	795	14
May	867	15
June	823	14
July	1067	18
August	854	15
September	288	5
October	100	2
November	53	1
December	9	0

See note for Question 1

Time of birth *Sample:* 5850

1 a.m.–1.59 a.m.	234	4
2 a.m.–2.59 a.m.	244	4
3 a.m.–3.59 a.m.	238	4
4 a.m.–4.59 a.m.	236	4
5 a.m.–5.59 a.m.	238	4
6 a.m.–6.59 a.m.	221	4
7 a.m.–7.59 a.m.	255	4
8 a.m.–8.59 a.m.	213	4
9 a.m.–9.59 a.m.	228	4
10 a.m.–10.59 a.m.	259	4
11 a.m.–11.59 a.m.	298	5
12 noon–12.59 p.m.	318	5
1 p.m.–1.59 p.m.	272	5
2 p.m.–2.59 p.m.	285	5
3 p.m.–3.59 p.m.	277	5
4 p.m.–4.59 p.m.	285	5
5 p.m.–5.59 p.m.	236	4
6 p.m.–6.59 p.m.	266	5
7 p.m.–7.59 p.m.	219	4

	Number	Percentage
8 p.m.–8.59 p.m.	255	4
9 p.m.–9.59 p.m.	224	4
10 p.m.–10.59 p.m.	188	3
11 p.m.–11.59 p.m.	189	3
12 midnight–12.59 a.m.	198	3

Day of the week		*Sample:* 5736
Monday	804	14
Tuesday	855	15
Wednesday	892	16
Thursday	899	16
Friday	923	16
Saturday	748	13
Sunday	615	11

Multiple births		*Sample:* 5914
1 baby	5891	100
Twins	22	0
Triplets	1	0

92 Was your baby born healthy? *Sample:* 5837

	Number	Percentage
Yes	5520	95
No	317	5

93 Was your baby kept in a special care baby unit?

Sample: 5762

	Number	Percentage
Yes	713	12
No	5040	87

If so, for how long?		*Sample:* 713
a) up to a day	281	39
b) 2–7 days	228	32
c) 8–14 days	62	9
d) more than 14 days	91	13

94 Did your baby have a check-up before leaving hospital?

Sample: 5571

	Number	*Percentage*
Yes	5423	97
No	138	2

95 How long did you stay in hospital? *Sample:* 5693

	Number	*Percentage*
a) up to 2 days	1483	26
b) 2–6 days	2440	43
c) more than 6 days	1766	31

96 Was your baby in the same room with you? *Sample:* 5762

	Number	*Percentage*
a) all the time	2293	40
b) some of the time	3278	57
c) none of the time	189	3

97 If your baby was taken away for any length of time, what was the main reason? *Sample:* 4329

	Number	*Percentage*
a) health (yours or the baby's)	646	15
b) your rest	2435	56
c) hospital routine	1133	26
d) other	76	2
e) don't know	10	0

98 Have you suffered any complications following the birth of your baby (e.g. infection)? *Sample:* 5692

	Number	*Percentage*
Yes	1256	22
No	4402	77

Depression

99 Have you suffered from postnatal depression?

Sample: 5721

	Number	*Percentage*
a) not at all	2857	50
b) a little	2668	47
c) a lot	181	3

100 If you have suffered from depression, were you offered any kind of treatment for it? *Sample:* 2011

a) medication?	*Number*	*Percentage*
Yes	204	10
No	1802	90

b) professional psychiatric help?		*Sample:* 1857
Yes	45	2
No	1806	97

101 If you have suffered from depression, who was the *best* person to talk to? *Sample:* 2340

	Number	*Percentage*
a) doctor	167	7
b) midwife	330	14
c) nurse	133	6
d) health visitor	242	10
e) friend or relative	969	41
f) other mothers with the same problem	212	9
g) no one	255	11

Breastfeeding

102 Were you encouraged to breastfeed your baby? *Sample:* 5653

	Number	*Percentage*
Yes	4652	82
No	965	17

If so, who influenced you the most?		*Sample:* 4652
a) doctor	356	8
b) midwife	1107	24
c) nurse	189	4
d) your mother	169	4
e) friend or relative	277	6
f) books or leaflets	317	7
g) your own initiative	2088	45

103 Do you or did you breastfeed your baby? *Sample:* 5730

	Number	*Percentage*
Yes	4738	83
No	986	17

104 Did you stop breastfeeding your baby? *Sample:* 5914

	Number	*Percentage*
Yes	1101	19
No	4813	81

If so, was it mainly . . . ? *Sample:* 1101

a) for health reasons (yours or the baby's)	188	17
b) your own wish	173	16
c) because you had trouble doing so	588	53
d) other	142	13

105 Did anyone help you to breastfeed? *Sample:* 5914

	Number	*Percentage*
Yes	3376	57
No	2538	43

If so, were they . . . ? *Sample:* 3376

a) helpful	2429	72
b) quite helpful	794	24
c) not at all helpful	141	4

Exercises

106 Do you know about doing postnatal exercises?

Sample: 5784

	Number	*Percentage*
Yes	5655	98
No	106	2

If so, who first advised you?*

	Number	Percentage
		Sample: 5655
a) doctor	181	3
b) midwife	1716	30
c) nurse	873	15
d) health visitor	279	5
e) friend or relative	76	1
f) books or leaflets	485	9
g) previous experience or general knowledge	1691	30

* We regret that 'physiotherapist' was omitted from the list of people who might have given advice about postnatal exercises. Many women added this piece of information to their forms.

Home

107 Do you or will you have any extra help in the home for the first week after you get home?

	Number	Percentage
		Sample: 5790
Yes	5078	88
No	705	12

108 Is your husband/partner . . . ?

	Number	Percentage
		Sample: 5511
a) helpful and understanding	4388	80
b) sometimes helpful and understanding	1051	19
c) not at all helpful and understanding	61	1

109 Have you been visited at home by a health visitor?

	Number	Percentage
		Sample: 5505
Yes	5281	96
No	223	4

110 Have you been visited at home by a midwife?

Sample: 5543

	Number	*Percentage*
Yes	5320	96
No	222	4

111 Have you been visited at home by your GP?

Sample: 5517

	Number	*Percentage*
Yes	3342	61
No	2165	39

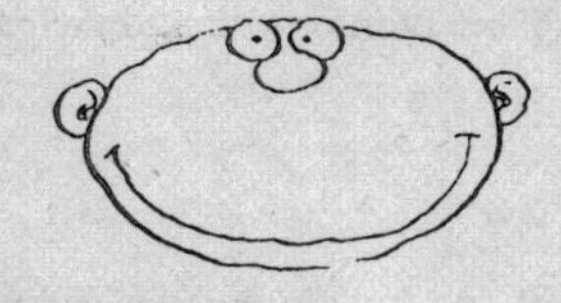